For
Anne Arundel County Public Library

TUGGING ON A HEARTSTRING THE SEQUEL

by

E. V. Lambert

SAN 298-7805
Marine Techniques Publishing
Augusta, Maine

Library of Congress Cataloging-in-Publication Data

Copyright © by Emily Vaughan Lambert, 1958
Tugging On A Heartstring The Sequel

    1st ed. 2009
         p.   cm.
    Includes biographical and personal accounts
    ISBN (10) 0-9798008-1-1
    ISBN (13) 978-0-9798008-1-8 (alk. paper)
    1. Expansive chronicle of E. V. Lambert's sea life
    2. Fair use (Copyright) United States. I. Lambert, Emily V.

Copyright Office, Library of Congress

Library of Congress Control Number 2008907988

ISBN 0-9798008-1-1   ISBN 978-0-9798008-1-8

Photographic/Images Property of: Emily V. Lambert

Cover production by TLC Graphics, Austin, Texas (Chelsea Shaw)

Printed in the United States of America

Marine Techniques Publishing
SAN 298-7805
126 Western Avenue, Suite 266
Augusta, ME 04330-7249 U.S.A.
(207) 622-7984 FAX: (207) 621-0821
Email: info@MarineTechPublishing.com
Web: www.MarineTechPublishing.com

Dedicated to Frank and Debbie Lambert

With special thanks to:

Mr. James L. Pelletier,
U.S. Merchant Marine Staff Officer and Marine Engineer *(Ret.)*

and

Captain Stewart W. Finch

Into the night, waves climb in ice,
against dawn light they burst;
and into my seaman's soul they're hushing:
"We were here first."

— *author*

TUGGING ON A HEARTSTRING: THE SEQUEL

The tugboat Pennsbury shouldered up the river like an ox.

Her bow spat out spray. Behind her lowered head, eighty feet of squared iron followed in reined power. She slowed at the head of the Nanticoke River in the rich salty air. She closed in on my sea family and our old tugboat Babe. As the Pennsbury closed in on us, she grew.

Growling alongside in the late summer of 1975, the Pennsbury was fifteen feet longer than Babe. She was ten feet wider and taller. She was a DPC class built in WWII for commerce on the Intercoastal Waterway to escape U-boat torpedoes. She had a breadth of twenty four feet and a depth of almost ten. We stood on tip-toes, on Babe's low deck, to reach Pennsbury's quarter bitts with our lines.

From her boxy, commanding wheelhouse, Dad was bellowing us into action. I held a wrist to my forehead, glancing into the sun at my captain. My older sister and I secured our lines in slow motion. Alison and I rubbed our noses with sadness.

"Okay, people!" Dad was saying as he descended Pennsbury's wheelhouse ladder. Flashing white, a seagull swooped behind Dad's six foot height as he said, "All of you people!"

Facing Dad and the powerful Pennsbury, we swelled hesitantly on Babe's familiar deck. Our good crew was Todd, our sereng or deck gang leader, and three teen boys: handsome and dark-eyed Mark; James with a long blonde braid down his back; and the slight and charming Georgia boy, Winn. "Everybody gets bourbon!" Dad commanded us. Brown inches solemnly filled the half dozen mismatched plastic cups and chipped galley mugs. We lifted them to Dad's plastic green cup: "To Babe." The whiskey burned aside my tears, in my sixteen year old throat.

Hours of tossing boxes and tools and work clothing from deck to deck followed. The hours were fleeting. It was over by dusk. As we finished and gathered on deck, Dad disappeared into the engine room. We stopped talking on deck. We listened for the last time to the cheery cry of Babe's engine starting: "A-woo-ga!"

Dad returned from the engine room and rested a hand on her rail. We had emptied Babe of our stuff, and now watched on sweat-faced and awkwardly. "Go, Mama," Dad muttered to the water. "Take her out." Mom pushed back her brunette hair and stepped up Babe's deck to the wheelhouse. We searched her face as she passed. Mom's hazel, tear-rimmed eyes were steady above her high chin.

We shifted on our bare feet self-consciously and looked up at our captain. Dad swept a muscular arm at the new tug. We followed his signal. We straddled the bulwark or foot rail to Pennsbury's wide deck.

"Hey!" laughed James. He nodded his blonde streaks into the doorway of the new galley. "This is the Ritz!" he said with an appreciative whistle, to which Alison and I shot him looks of disgust before resuming our mournful ones.

Dad dug Pennsbury's heavy hocks into reverse. The current creased below our feet. Across the deep-blue river, Babe sat naked against the dock. She was alone now with her high, proud bow. Her brooms and mops, linens and charts and daughterly voices were gone. Above our heads, Pennsbury's deep, bass stack sniffed leisurely off the river banks.

In the following sweep of silence, Babe returned with her murmur of life. A gray puff fell from her black stack. Mom guided her from the dock, and Babe's years tumbled at me across the channel. Her tapered back wheelhouse, and graceful 1906-built lines, had protected me and my family in how many winter gales? I frowned across the river, fighting down the wild sob in my throat.

I jumped. With a confident, contained snort from her stack above my head, the Pennsbury pierced the silence of the shadowy forest banks. She slid passed the Babe. She took up the open dock. We secured her with lines while Dad closed down the big engine.

Mom brought Babe gently to the outside rail. Dad boarded, and they took Babe downriver by themselves.

Behind the huge H-bitt on Pennsbury's stern, not touching its fat iron, I watched my parents and Babe departing. Babe's slender green house jumped and fell through my tears until she glided behind a forest bend and was gone.

...   .

"Hey, Em!" Alison hollered down the deck. "Can you believe this bunkroom?"

I blew my nose into my T-shirt. I squeezed a salty pinch of Copenhagen into my lip, and dragged my feet up Pennsbury's big, wide deck.

The deck rake was gentle. The rake had a lower and more modern angle than Babe's. I passed several doorways from the stern on the starboard deck, including a head with a real shower and a real door. I met Alison forward at the cook's fo'c'sle. It was just aft the galley door.

"We got a screened door, Em!"

I admired the mesh in my fingertips as I stepped over the coaming into the fo'c'sle.

"And look, Em! We got our own lockers and a shelf, for stuff!"

"This sink's mighty fancy," I admitted reluctantly. I squinted into the mirror above the sink at my green eyes and tangled blonde hair, and spat into the sink drain.

"Yea, our own sink!" Alison rejoiced. Her blue eyes squeezed with bursting excitement over her freckled nose. "And look overhead," she squeaked.

"A fan..." I hushed. "We got our own fan..." The dusty ten-inch appliance was bolted neatly to the bulkhead above the sink. It pointed to the double wooden bunks. In all of Babe's belowdecks, there was but one fan, in the galley. Alison and I smiled at each other and back to the fan, as if the modern convenience would disappear if we blinked.

"Emily," a restrained voice spoke slowly through the screened door. "You are cook. Come to the galley."

I followed our six foot-two sereng up the deck.. "Alison and I have our own fan, Todd!" I told his broad back.

Todd said nothing. He stepped inside the galley and extended a long arm to the floor. "Look." I followed his arm. There was a square hole in the deck. Between the galley table and the bulkhead, a steep iron ladder ran down the hole. "Don't fall down that," warned Todd a little unnecessarily. "And look."

He unhooked the hatch cover from the side of the table. He lowered it over the hole and then, grunting from the weight, hooked it open again. "This hatch cover weighs thirty pounds. Hook it open properly or it will fall on your head. Now let's go down."

Pennsbury's forepeak was stacked with goods, boxed, bagged, canned, and bottled. A person could live off the goods for a year, I thought, even before Todd opened a long freezer on the portside. He lifted its cover to show high stacks of meat. Along the starboard bulkhead were coiled lines, lanterns, come-alongs, and other deck implements.

Scrunching my shoulders away from the safely hooked hatch cover, I climbed out of the forepeak and faced the stove. It was broader than Babe's with a modern-looking motor to control diesel flow. A large, stainless steel sink adjacent the stove was followed by counter space and a businesslike refrigerator, double the size of Babe's with two doors.

A table filled the width of the forward galley. The table bench was a slow u-shape of cushions against the bulkhead. There were several portholes. I was admiring the two large fans bolted strategically above them until Todd's perfect nose and perfect mouth, under a sharp cut of combed brown hair, interrupted my view. "Come to the engine room now," said Todd.

Just inside the heat and bright lights of the engine room, Todd was trying to draw my attention to a hand-crank pump. I was much more impressed with an actual water fountain beside us on the upper catwalk. It was like in school hallways. I pushed its silvery floor pedal with my callused toes. Water gushed up. It was icy! My full cheeks dribbled water down my chin as I ran rounded eyes over the huge engine room. Two ladders descended port and starboard from the catwalk. The engine, stretching far forward, was an 800 GM locomotive. Dials glittered fore and aft.

Our new 800 locomotive engine

I felt a quick, impatient tap on my shoulder. Todd pointed to the hand crank at the forward bulkhead and spoke over the generator's roar below.

"You have to pump up the diesel intake for the stove every morning. Do you understand?" I swallowed my gulp of icy water and nodded. "Make sure this cock is open, and wind the crank, here, like this." Todd demonstrated in wide, muscular loops with the crank handle. "Read this pump gauge, here, and stop when this needle is at this red mark. Do you understand?" I nodded again. "Then, of course, re-close the fuel cock."

Again I nodded. I held up an okay sign with my fingers.

Todd lifted his chin. "It's very important to re-close the cock," he repeated pretty unnecessarily.

"Roger. Re-close the cock."

Not quite satisfied with his instructions for the stove's diesel, Todd looked me up and down skeptically with his hands on his hips.

"I'll make sure to re-close the cock, Todd," I reassured him, and patted my pockets for my tobacco tin to cover up my rising impatience. Sweat trickled down both our faces from the heat of the engine room.

Finally, Todd jabbed a firm thumb at the deck. "Get supper started. There will be two more men coming with us in our trip to Norfolk."

I stepped over the coaming to see Mom's smile floating down the deck. "What do you think, lovey?"

"She's real big, Ma!" I said, wiping the sweat off my face with my T-shirt. "I'm makin' supper in the new galley!" But my smile faded. "Where's Babe?"

"Give me a hug, lamb chop," Mom sang softly. She wrapped her arm around my waist and we stepped up the deck. "You'll see her. She's docked in Vienna. I think the new owner is taking her to Philadelphia."

I looked over my shoulder downriver. A red beacon light darted out from the darkness.

"Hey, Ma!" Alison called out from the cook's fo'c'sle. "Pretty neat, Ma!"

Mom laughed and said, "Come to the galley, Al. Help us cook up a meal for the men."

...　　...　　...　　...　　...

Aubrey said that he hailed from a descendent pirate population on the Carolina Outer Banks. At least, that's what I thought he said.

In the confusion of storms, lanterns would be placed by the pirates along a beach to lure ships. Unfortunate vessels would confuse the lanterns as aids to navigation and wreck. The land pirates collected the washed up cargo on the beaches. They were a geographically isolated group. Their dialect reflected this into modern times. We couldn't understand a word Aubrey said.

The wiry deckhand was aboard to teach us about the Pennsbury, a vessel he had sailed for many years.

Also aboard was Captain Calvert, an older friend of Dad's and a former schooner captain. He was making one trip south to relieve Dad at the wheel while Dad learned the new GM.

14

Around Captain Calvert's eyes, wrinkles had deepened from years of navigating the sea, but I was uncomfortable to find him frowning at me. I slid a plate of broccoli and lemon, potatoes, and a ten inch wide steak in front of him that night. He shoved the plate back and snapped, "Gimme a third o' that! You gimme too much!" I admired the captain, and his clear disapproval of women on the water was hurtful to me. The water was my home. As I cut his steak in half, I wished Captain Calvert would take his disapproval, one grown man to another, one deck up.

Thankfully, there was a lot of room aboard the Pennsbury.

Alison and I had our private fo'c'sle, aft the galley. The boys and two guests had two fo'c'sles astern with single bunks, and the portside fo'c'sle with double bunks. An on-watch man created an empty berth.

Up above, the captain's cabin offered Mom and Dad, at long last, a large, single bunk; a real desk with wooden cabinets; a private door to the upper deck; and their own fresh water sink under which, however, was the familiar bucket.

We flew to Norfolk.

An eighteen hour arrival time snapped by us, with a loaded barge, at seven knots! The same run took a day and a half with our Babe. And now we were steaming at seven knots! Tug Pennsbury wasn't Babe, I thought, but she sure was impressive.

I mentioned my admiration halfway south the next day in the filling galley. A morning sun buttered the tile floor. The passing wash shivered its reflections onto my bare feet and across the galley ceiling. I swung a wet dish towel over my shoulder and looked out at the brightening bay. "I already see Wolf Trap!" I sighed with a sweaty shake of my head.

Aubrey leaned through the doorway. His dark eyes darted back and forth in his thin, weathered face. "She'm pretty, aright- 'n yo' git'n t'a fly'n, a'righ!" He drained his coffee mug with a swagger and looked proud.

I leaned forward. "Pardon?" I smiled.

We were all smiles through coffee steam in the bright, promising dawn. The water chuckled silvery under the gunnels. My heart danced with the openness. For most of my young life, the beauty and freedom of the water was as normal and day-to-day as the harsh privilege of surviving it.

With a full heart, I turned to the wall of Todd's chest. He had centered himself with a slow lurch in the galley. He leaned his arm high against the steering cable column in the ceiling. He was the only crewman tall enough to lean against it. His other arm, trailing a mile of smudged diesel, dangled down to a hooked thumb in his khakis. On top of his towering body, over my frying pans and slopping dishwater, was a scowl. He only lacked a bull whip, I sniffed, with an antebellum or prewar show of indifference.

The sereng threw his eyes at sleepy-faced James, posed vaguely at the table over an empty space. It was 0630. Todd liked his day watch on deck by 0630, no matter how new the galley was to me. I ducked under his elbow to glare, in turn, at the sizzling frying pans. But the hot diesel stove was a hot diesel stove. My temperature rose, and I lifted a glare way up to Todd. Completely unimpressed, he continued to stare at my now-curled lip.

I eventually bought him off with a plate of sausage, fresh eggs, cottage cheese, apple butter, and toast, and skidded the same under James' bobbing nose.

"Todd hovers, Mom!" I cried in the wheelhouse. "He hovers!"

"There, there, dearie. My, what a delicious breakfast you've brought us!"

"Daddy, Todd -"

"He's just doin' his job, gal. Where's my spoon for my eggs?"

"I forgot your spoon, Daddy! 'Cause Todd was hovering -"

"Emmo, please get a spoon for your Papa."

"But Todd's terrible! And Al 'n me only spit on him twice last week! I swear! 'N he didn't even notice the one in his hair -"

"Emily, don't spit chew on the sereng. Debbie, I want my spoon."

"But, Ma! Dad!"

"Emmo!"

Atop the wheelhouse ladder, author as young teen in her galley apron

I returned with a spoon and a slouch.

Over Mom's and Dad's shoulders, bowed to the thick porcelain   plates in their laps, a radio rattled off weather data from the aft shelf. The new wheel house had a slat shelf to secure the binoculars, next to chart racks and book shelves. The engine consoles were bigger, with a new radar and autopilot, under more and bigger windows. The mate's stool was backed! Gone were the handholds on the ceiling, so imperative to our faithful Babe's winter wheelhouse.

"Want to try 'er, Emmo?"

"I can steer? Really, Daddy?"

He laughed. "Soon enough it'll be just another dull old watch for ye."

I slipped between Mom and the port bulkhead. Clutching her arm with excitement, I curled dishwater-pruned fingers around the black steering knob. I gave a wide-eyed smile to Mom, and the steering knob the same.

"It's just like Babe's, honey," she said, and jabbed her toast into some sparkling, purple jam.

It was just like Babe's. The steering levers, set below the window sills, moved horizontally in an inward arc. They moved aft

17

for port, and forward for starboard. Testing the Pennsbury's steering, I happily added quarter mile zigzags to our wake before Dad looked up from his plate and said something under his breath I couldn't make out.

An actual steering wheel was centered in front of the compass. Painted in gray gloss paint like the rest of the wheelhouse, the wheel came up to my shoulders. I was happy to give up steering for a whimsical moment, and stand at the helm of an ocean-going freighter. I tried to spin the wheel in weathered know-how.

"The wheel's tied down," Dad said with a yawn and handed me his empty plate.

I frowned ahead with the plate, one more emergency as I saved my ship from crashing onto the Rock of Gibraltar. And it was a surprise to feel all at once dizzy for our height and pace over the water. We were doing seven knots with a loaded tow! This was a speed for other tugboats, forever passing us by, until now!

...   .

We steamed south into a building headwind. Pennsbury took on the lower bay with ease. She plowed through the chop with her 146 gross tons.

A breeze scampered through the galley's screened doors. Reeking of chalky-sweet Lava soap, Alison and the men stepped over the coamings for supper.

Winn paused at the stove. He pulled a wet arm across his oily T-shirt and said, "Smells awf'ly nice, Em'ly."

"Why, Winn..." My fingers darted in my oven mitts to my braids. "Thank you," I sighed at the curly-haired boy. He cast down his soft hazel eyes, and smiled, before easing behind the dark green table.

I turned around, a bit aglow, for the orchestration of the meal. Behind my stirring, knee-dipping, reaching, and different crashes, I picked up on the conversation. The men had been down below most of the day. I loaded the table with mounds of mashed potatoes and platters of fried chicken as questions and answers went back and forth about our new 800 diesel, with four to one reduction. Aubrey, Captain Calvert, Todd, and Mark held the general dialogue, with an occasionally trilling and expansive, "Ahhhh! So that thing's for the generator?" from the only other girl ordinary seaman probably in the United States. "Why, James, look at that cut on your hand!" I heard Alison's interest veering away as Winn stood quickly, and smiled slowly, to open the screened door for me. I blushed with appreciation and stepped on deck with my wheelhouse plates.

"Captain Calvert getting everything he needs there, girl?"

I had stalled for the doorway breeze on the wheelhouse landing. "Oh, yes, Daddy. But, I don't think he -"

"Debbie, somebody with the knowledge of that man is downright marvelous."

"But Daddy, I don't think he likes girls on boats. I don't think-"

"Don't you fret about the ways of old schooner captains, Emmo." Dad inhaled a forkful of carrots in a glaze of brown sugar. "Five degrees port," he said through a swallow.

"'Scuse, Ma." I reached to the steering knob over her propped up toes, which I gave a mischievous pinch.

"Emily!" Mom shrieked, and her dinner plate jumped in her lap.

"Woman, are you listening to me?"

"Yes, Papa!"

While Dad talked to Mom of his newly gained engine room knowledge, I steered a southerly course toward Willoughby Spit. Dad had taken us off autopilot because of the traffic. He interrupted his dinner conversation with Mom to make and receive radio calls. The twinkling of vessel lights increased in number against the southern sky.

I knew a tug had three important sets of navigational lights. The red and green wheelhouse running lights were constant features of an underway tug. The white stern light on the upper deck was a constant feature, too. The third set of lights rose on a mast above the tangle of the radar and searchlight apparatus on the wheelhouse roof.

One light burning on the mast indicated a tug was light and had no tow. Two mast lights indicated the tug was pushing a vessel, forward or on the hip. Three lights indicated a tow in progress. Not too many summers passed before someone died on a recreational craft from getting clothes-lined by a hawser. They would fail to understand a tug's three white mast lights. The following barge, with its own required running lights, would be mistaken as a separately steaming vessel.

As Mom and Dad ate supper and I steered our southerly course, I could see a gray freighter building up steam for sea from Norfolk. The ship looked coral-colored from the melting red sunset behind it.

I lifted the binoculars and watched the vessel swing its mammoth length eastward for the Atlantic. The bridge wing showed a red light. I knew the starboard wing was showing green. Like on a tugboat, the ship's running lights were visible to two points abaft beam, or to "eight o'clock" on the portside and "four o'clock" on the starboard.

I shifted my binoculars. I could see a white light above the ship's bridge. I could see another, lower white light at the bow. These were the ship's two range lights. The bow range light was visible to two points abaft the beam, and the range light above the bridge was visible all around.

I knew it was vital for passing traffic to read a ship's range lights. When the two lights appeared far apart, one was viewing the ship from abeam. The closer the range lights appeared to each other, the more acute the head-on angle of the ship. As my old sereng, Zeke, taught me, if a ship's range lights ever appeared as one, it was time to jump.

...   .

Mom and I left the wheelhouse dishes in the galley and joined the crew in the stern. It was time to haul in the hawser before making port.

Aubrey was gesticulating, with flying limbs, the procedure about to begin. Jabbering through a cigarette in his dancing dialect, the deckhand was enjoying his captive audience. He would stop now and then, rub his bare chest as he listened to a question, and then start gesturing again. The boys nodded when Aubrey exhaled, "Ya'll see?" and laughed when he bounded something off his tongue to a slap of his thin knee.

Above us, in his stained T-shirt and tattered khaki shorts, Dad stood with a puffed out chest. His bottom lip was jutted out. He was going to use his stern controls for the first time.

A steering and engine control column stood beside him at the upper deck railing. He shoved the knobs about in his bear-paw hands, pausing to absorb their effect on our drift. His stolid gaze, alive with suppressed excitement, fell from his bifocals to the crowded deck below. "This boat's all right, Aubrey."

"Ga'dat, Frank!"

"Let's get that bitch off the string."

Frank at his upper deck stern controls

Alison and I squealed with excitement. Dad didn't curse unless he was angry, pleased, tired, or hungry. And pleasure was written all over his proud, squared shoulders as he twisted ahead on his bare feet, and stretched to look back, from his new stern controls.

The Pennsbury only bounced a hair as we reversed neatly over the chop. The late dusk outlined us in soft steel-gray until Aubrey reached behind the H-bitt. A powerful white beam lit up the stern. Our tan, excited faces suddenly looked pale and sepulchral.

The engine slowed. Todd pulled on the hawser. He nodded up at Frank with a squint into the white light.

Aubrey joined him at the H-bitt. They freed the wraps and quickly dragged the hawser to the starboad side. The crew bunched around Aubrey to see him work the capstan. Aubrey looped the hawser on the giant ribbed mushroom. He flipped a switch on the bulkhead and the capstan began to rotate and whine loudly.

After years of bowing our backs to the saturated three-strand nylon rope, a machine was hauling the hawser for us. Alison gave a prissy look to her fingernails and I leaned back on the H-bitt with a loud, bored sigh. Then we grabbed each other's arms and laughed, and Mom got a surprise daughter-sandwich hug.

The Lambert family's new capstan

The men led the hawser from the capstan into table coils. Gasps now punctuated Aubrey's indiscernible dialogue. We watched his weathered hands and their confident skill. Aubrey would be off in a few days; we needed to be familiar with the new machinery to avoid mistakes and injury.

Aubrey seemed well-aware of this. He tapped me on the arm and pointed to the pushing cable winch wheels. "Sta' clee'o d'em!" he rasped through his tobacco-stained teeth. "Sta' clee'!"

...   .

We finished our trip with a prim barge docking under Pensbury's sure power. Slipping through the gusty night waters, we left the granary and radioed ahead for a spot at the Texaco dock.

Aubrey led us through the procedures for fuel and fresh water. To our surprise, there were deck gaskets for both fuel and water. For fresh water on the Babe, a hose was wound below into the forepeak with someone stationed with a plumb line at the tank. Babe held 600 gallons of water and 4,000 gallons of diesel fuel. The Pennsbury held 3,000 gallons of water and 20,000 of diesel.

Captain Calvert, Aubrey, and Dad worked below after fueling and long after I had faded off to sleep. The old schooner captain was due at another vessel at the crack of dawn. He had called a cab and left before I washed up and started breakfast. I was glad to have missed the last of his quick frowns at my legs and black bare feet.

But we had all enjoyed a full, sound sleep without watches. The artificial brightness of the fuel dock had been reassuring on the new boat. A warm southerly wind had blown jubilantly through the night, but our ride against the pier was gentle with Pennsbury's bumpers. They were piled rubber slats on cable reaching down to her waterline. There were five of these sixty pound elephant noses spaced down both sides of the tug. Underway, to cut down on drag, we hauled the bumpers aboard, one person to a bumper, and years of developed strength helped.

Giving assistance in the southern bay

Sailing at early dawn, we muscled aboard the bumpers and steamed under the skyscrapers of Norfolk, lifeless in the soft pink sky. We had no tow. We sped free into the southern bay until we heard a distress call. We changed course to assist a broken down white tug, with a crane barge, off Cape Charles. We were able to resume our northward course by late morning.

"Leef'a ri' dere. Don' wosh'a."

I forced a smile and nodded. An eleven o'clock sun licked flames across the galley floor. Perspiration spun off my face onto the gritty pages of Joy of Cooking. Our wake roared and danced past the doorway. Aubrey turned down Pennsbury's deck and, through the sun spots in my eyes from the empty doorway, I flung my twelve pound bird into a roasting pan.

Close living quarters brought out private quirks like a magnifying glass. Aubrey's was to leave a coffee mug on the galley counter all day for his frequent cups.

For a couple of days now, the solitary mug beaded up from my scrubbed counters. Aubrey had milk and sugar with his coffee, promising a cloud of flies around the sticky mug. He would say through the flies, "Leef'a ri' d'ere. Don' bodda t'wosh eet."

"Huh? What?" I'd squint at him. "Whatchya say?"

It was hard to say goodbye, however, when Aubrey got off in

24

Seaford. We had lived and worked beside him in the isolation of the water, and the resulting bond was always special and somehow lifelong.

Our grain barge Deborah

There was a circle of handshakes and last minute indiscernible instructions from the deckhand. After Aubrey's final wave, an odd mixture of relief and regret seemed to fill the boat. We made up to our loaded barge. Much slower than our northward trip, we steamed into the open bay.

We were now on our own, on the tugboat Pennsbury.

...   .

Captain Frank did have a powerful new tug. But Dad was notorious for his tackling of life. I thought about Dad's determination with rising alarm after we docked our grain barge in Norfolk. Standing on Pennsybury's deck, I watched our approach to an oil barge almost 300 feet in length.

Our crew stood on the bow buzzing over the details of the job. We were sailing to the anchorage to lighter a ship. Laden tankers pumped off to barges in the anchorage to attain proper harbor draft.

Nervously folding our arms or scratching ears that didn't itch, our crew stood by on the bow deck. Lightering was a change from hauling grain, but reading the doubtful expressions on deck, no one seemed prepared for a change of this magnitude. I loaded in a pinch of Copenhagen and breathed a silent prayer that the Pennsbury would aim for a smaller barge.

Our approach on the giant remained steady. We powered into its shadow.

Late summer brought a surprising chill to the afternoon. Our crew looked more civilized in sweatshirts from being half-naked for so many months. We were momentarily more formal to each other because of it. Mom joined us from the wheelhouse, and I snuggled up in her soft, faded blue sweatshirt at the ladder.

"Mama! Brrr!"

"I know, Emmo! Yes, love," she laughed as she reached for the centerline coil. "And now we must move the barge, dear."

"Mother," I said gravely. "It's a very large barge."

She lifted her chin and looked off our bow. Mom often gave a slight smile when we faced pending adventure, and her show of composure, always a statement of her faith in Dad, was familiar to me. Hugging her soft sweatshirt, however, I had heard her heartbeat.

We could have entered a railroad tunnel as Pennsbury slid into the pushing chock.

There was a ladder welded onto the stern of the barge. Winn ascended the ladder with quick feet. We tossed the pushing cable lashings up to him after several attempted throws and vigorous slacking at the winches. Winn stood more than a dozen feet above us.

As we threw the lashings up to him, a chilling fact loomed to face us: we wouldn't be able to see over the barge and its tankerman's shack. The chock curved far back and swallowed us to our galley doors. The lower panes of Pennsbury's wheelhouse windows reflected the high, black barge hull.

I was soon dragging the chair out of my fo'c'sle and arguing it through the doorway to Todd. Todd hoisted it over his shoulders to the upper deck. Like ascending a wedding cake, James lifted the chair to the wheelhouse roof. I stood on the foot rail and aimed a spit at the base of a very tall, tarry piling. I squinted overhead again. On the wheelhouse roof, the sky emptied a little when Dad sat down in the chair.

A thick wire fell from his wrist. I saw it when he leaned over the roof. He looked down and said, "Get those lines off."

Winn and James hurried up the barge ladder after Todd.

Alison was quick to leap out of their path. Dad called down to her bobbing brown ponytails, "Get down to the engine room and check that oil pressure like I showed ye! Where's Emily?" I leaned far back to see the wheelhouse roof. "Git up here, gal!"

Alison and I threw ourselves into our destinations and into each other on the deck. "Eek!" we gasped in turn. I untangled my baggy sweatshirt from the galley door dog while Alison spun aft. "Eek!" I heard her cry again as Toto rounded the stern deck playfully and joined in the excitement with her barking.

"Talk between me and Debbie," Dad was instructing me on the upper deck. "Be goddamn clear."

"Roger, Frank!" I answered. I hoisted myself onto the upper deck guardrail with my bare feet dangling. I stretched up my fingertips and pressed them for balance against the wheelhouse roof eave.

"Here we go," Dad grumbled from the roof.

"Here we go!" I dipped down and screamed into the wheelhouse window at Mom's pale face: only Dad operated the engine controls!

"Tell Mama slow astern."

"Slow astern, roger!" I lowered my head to the window again. "Slow astern!"

"Emmo!" Mom shrieked at the engine lever with her hands clasped to her chest and her chin pulled away, as if the lever was made of something hideous. She delicately pulled it back.

"Oh! Slow astern!"

"Slow astern!" I repeated with equal horror overhead.

"Roger," Dad's voice answered from somewhere on the roof. The wire of the starboard steering lever extended several yards from the wheelhouse window and up to the roof. I could hear the click of the lever in Dad's hands. "Neutral," he said.

"Neutral, Ma!"

Mom carefully slipped the steel lever into its center notch.

"Neutral!" I screamed into the sky.

"Slow ahead."

"Slow ahead, Ma!"

"Oh! Oh! Oh!"

All at once the grossly huge piling I had spit at started slipping away from our rail. We were actually moving the giant barge.

"Ah, Emmo?"

"Yes, Dad!"

"Get me something to drink. What d'ya have in the galley?"

"Drink?" I shrieked. Dad peered down at me. "Um, l-lemonade."

"Okay, get me some lemonade. And tell Mama to add a little steam before you go."

"Ma! A little faster!"

"Okay," she replied tensely and, with two hands, carefully pressed the control forward.

"I'm gettin' Dad somethin' to drink! Do you want anythin'?" Mom shook her head with wide eyes. "I'll be right back," I assured her. "We're doin' great!" cracked my voice.

"We are going to die!" Alison cried flying into the galley. She jumped next to me and smacked my arm and spilled the lemonade. "Do you realize we have to dock this thing at a ship?" she shouted into my face. "Not at a dock! At a ship!"

"I know! I know!" my voice wavered as I slammed shut the refrigerator door and grabbed Dad's green plastic cup from the counter. "I gotta get back and relay!"

Securing the plastic cup on the roof of the captain's cabin, I climbed the ladder forward of Pennsbury's belching stack. The dizzy view grew when I climbed the next ladder to the wheelhouse roof. I stood behind Dad. Hoses, pipes, and wheel cranks scattered ahead over an acreage of black surface. I could see the boys, looking like stick figures, dragging and coiling lines that looked like threads. Passing navigational aids disappeared from view under the sides of the massive barge.

The lemonade slopped and trickled as Dad set it down by his bare feet. I stood mesmerized by the scene when he suddenly said, "It's that bastard pirate." His eyes were on the starboard bow and a rusty old bay boat. "He should know to stay clear, but he can see I'm blinder th'n a bat. I don't like it. Tell Debbie to radio that bastard. Take him on two whistles. Hurry, gal."

Mom and Alison jumped when I yelled out the name of the notorious captain. He was known for seedy waterfront deals and shanghaiing drunken seamen. "Frank says take 'im on two whistles!"

"Hey, gal!" Dad called down to me.

I lifted my chin to the eave. "Talk on the speaker and get Todd back here. We're coming up on the ship."

"Alison," I whispered into the wheelhouse, over Mom's even voice into the radio mike. "Call Todd! We're almost at the ship!"

Alison adjusted the wheelhouse intercom to speaker and picked up the mike. "Todd? Todd?" Her young voice echoed back from the surrounding barge chock.

"Roger, two whistles, and thank you, captain," Mom was finishing. "Tug Pensbury, WF8912, out."

"Okay, Todd!" Dad's powerful voice carried over the turbulence of the barge wake. "Here we go with this thing. Your boys awake up there?" I looked up and saw Todd hold a closed fist in the air. He held it. "Got your two bow lines and two stern lines?" Todd's fist jabbed the air. "I got to get me a line, Todd, first try - roger me?" The fist jumped. "They've got to be goddamn sure awake up there! And I need clear signals from you, Mr. Todd! Are you ready for this thing?" The fist jabbed the air several times. "Okay, roger."

Our sereng spun around and strode forward against the growing silhouette of a seven hundred foot foreign flag tanker.

"Tell Debbie to slow down again, just above neutral." Dad's directions were coming fast.

The Pennsbury's stack lowered to a gapped growl.

"Neutral!" Dad shouted.

I repeated, "Neutral, Ma!" and our decks went smooth of vibration.

"Okay, okay," I could hear Dad murmur to himself. He was twisting back in the chair and looking over the side. "What's our tide doin', little girl?" I looked down from my rail perch. The water was dark green in the twilight. It slapped against us white tips. "Ah, tell Debbie to reverse. Reverse a couple notches."

"Reverse two notches, Debbie!"

"Reverse two notches, roger!"

"Tell Todd I want a bow line first!" Dad shouted. "Get on the speaker!"

"Roger! Alison!" I yelled into the wheelhouse. "Tell Todd bow line first!"

Her light voice trickled over the speaker in waves and echoed off the ship. The ship's mast lights burned above us. A red light held a calm halo on the range light mast. It indicated the loading or discharging of dangerous cargo.

"Tell that man I need more distance signals starting right now!"

"Al!" I shouted into the wheelhouse. "Tell Todd to signal distance more!"

She grabbed the mike. "Todd! Frank needs more hand signals! We can't see a thing!" she added with exasperation at the wall of barge chock.

"Crank 'er back! I need full astern!"

"Full astern, Mama!"

"Heavens!" she gasped and pulled back the iron lever hard to growing thunder from Pennsbury's stack and spreading vibrations of the engine through our feet.

"Neutral!"

"Neutral, Ma!"

"Did you get it?" Dad shouted and stood. He knocked over his cup of lemonade. The green plastic cup dove over the deck eave and clattered sharply at my feet on the upper deck. "Stern line! Stern line!" Dad bellowed across to the jumbo barge. "You, girl!

Tell Debbie slow ahead!"

"Slow ahead, Debbie!" I repeated, and added with a squeal, "I think we got a line!"

Mom pressed the lever gently forward while Alison hugged her waist. Mom's shoulders dropped a little. "We got a line, girls," she breathed.

"Neutral!" I heard above me. "Where are you, Emily?"

"Neutral!" I yelled into the wheelhouse.

Mom jumped, and centered the engine control. We peered overhead, above the black wall of chock. Judging from the ship's mast lights in the sky, we must have secured our lines outboard another lightering barge.

Dad's big bulk was suddenly taking up the center of the wheehouse. He was tenderly holding Mom's face in his hands. "We did it, baby. We did it."

Mom looked up into Dad's eyes in the wheelhouse, and as they kissed, Alison and I knew they were not on the tugboat Pennsbury at all.

··· ··· ··· ··· ···

Like jolly, grimy chimney sweeps, crews from neighboring tugs in the operation came and went. They jumped down in big, dirty work shoes. They made conversation in our galley and made faces over our coffee, known as the worse brewed on the bay despite of, or maybe because of, our experimental egg shells in our low cost coffee grounds.

We shifted our barge against the ship at ten o'clock that night.

As dawn opened over the operation, I could see men darting across our barge to monitor hoses from the ship. The ends of hardware were clamped at points across the settling barge which now, though slowly, read higher and higher Plimsoll lines.

After breakfast, I straddled our foot rail with a bowl of potatoes. My potato skins spun into the ship's shadow. Pulling my apron over my knees to hide my legs, I discreetly peered overhead. What did it feel like to steer this great vessel? How did she respond to a port lever, slow astern, a three foot chop, a twenty foot sea? My potatoes peels drifted and bumped against her hull and my eyes rose curiously to the deck. Who were those men in her crew, akin to me like distant cousins, in the bloodline of the sea? Knotted brown locks framed their faces of dark beard stubble as they grinned and exchanged foreign cigarettes for magazines with our crew.

Watching the men interact so freely, I bowed my shoulders slightly forward to hide my shape when they looked down. The effect was melancholy. I knew that sailing beyond the Chesapeake Bay as a merchant seawoman was an unreachable dream for me.

Or was it?

The big oil barge was only four feet above the waterline when the fuel hoses were craned to the decks of the rising ship. Our visibility would be excellent now.

We departed the ship's side with newly squared shoulders. We spat and kidded on deck. The first half of our lightering journey, and the toughest part we knew, had been met with success by the Lambert Tug Co., Inc.. Our Pennsbury swaggered confidently into the channel with the loaded barge. There, her growling engine, chugging stack, and healthy, vibrating decks became all at once as silent as attic dust.

My dicing knife stopped midair over a celery stalk. I threw down my knife with a pinched cry. Bodies were rushing passed the galley doors and feet were pounding down the decks. Then it was silent again. With a chill in my stomach, I scrambled on deck and onto a quarterbitt.

Our thrashing wake astern had already smoothed and disappeared. Spinning my head forward, there was a line of ships docked at a pier ahead. I could see our barge was drifting out of the channel toward them. I clamped my wet, celery-smelling fingers over my mouth to muffle my shriek: we were gliding toward the bow of a docked freighter! I jumped down on deck and tore up the wheelhouse ladder.

"Mama!"

"I've got no steering!" Mom's voice was high-pitched and

shaky. "Papa has to fix the engine!"

Alison raced in the opposite door. "Mama!" she cried, and clutched the back of Mom's blue sweatshirt. I clutched the back of Alison's shirt, and cried into their faces, "We're gonna collide with that ship!"

Ahead of us, the sea-beaten orange freighter was sleepily secure at its dock. The ship was resting at its dock with, apparently, an alarming amount of trust that the surrounding harbor traffic would not hit it.

Mom, Alison, and I leaned forward with scrunched up shoulders. We held each other, trembling, as Mom's fingers circled the steering knob. She pulled it back for port direction. She pulled it back again, and again. Our big barge only lumbered stubbornly to starboad. We were not clearing the pier. We were heading further into it. The freighter's bow flare sat silently ahead.

My nose was an inch from Mom's chin. "Tell Frank," she enunciated slowly to me word for word, "that we need the engine to be working."

"Roger!" I yelled at the bow stem on the lower deck as I was already skidding on bare palms down the wheelhouse ladder to a dead run down the deck.

"Frank!" The engine room was quiet. "Daddy!" I hollered from the catwalk. "Ma wants to know when the engine will go!"

A tool clanked hollowly on the deck plates below. "Ah, give me that one there, Todd," Dad said quietly, and then, "Emily, tell Mama we're working as fast as we can."

I jumped back from the engine room door and lifted a foot to sprint up the deck. I spun around. "Dad?" I gulped. "There's a pier with ships-"

"Tell your Ma we're working as fast as we can."

Dad seemed unnaturally calm to me, like the unnatural calm before a summer squall. I turned anxiously from the engine room and climbed onto the foot rail. Dead ahead, the ship's midsection could have been the abyss that would swallow my family's entire world.

Mom and Alison searched my face when I returned to the

wheelhouse. With many blinks, they turned back to the freighter. Our feet shifted nervously. Without the engine roaring upward through the bulkheads and decks, we could hear our feet calluses rasping against the sunsprayed wheelhouse floor.

"Alison..." Mom swallowed. "Go see..."

I scrambled below after her. Our shoulders pressed against each other in the engine room doorway.

"We're working as fast as we can, Alison."

Alison ripped up the deck to the wheelhouse and I leapt aside at the galley. I stood over the defrosting pork chops in the sink. There was only one thing to do: I smothered the pork chops in celery stuffing and slammed them into the diesel oven.

What next? We were closing in on an ocean-going ship with a runaway oil barge! I made a blueberry cheesecake pie!

The grocery store mixes and cans never heard such salty dialogue as I ran a shivering finger down Betty Crocker's cheerful instructions and combined the ingredients in lightning speed. I slammed the pie into the refrigerator. I clutched the galley doorway. I forced myself back on deck where I could now distinguish the shadows in the curves of the ship's propeller blades.

Alison stood beside Mom in the wheelhouse, heaving for air after another dash below. Their eyes ran over my face, found no answers, and furiously jumped forward again. I joined the relay to the engine room and found the same measured response. Dad was systematically deducting the problem back on an unfamiliar 800 diesel!

"Call 'em, Ma! Call 'em!" Alison was saying from the wheel-house landing.

"We have'ta, Ma!" I said. I pointed a blueberry-stained finger out the wheelhouse window. "We're gonna collide with- !"

"Yes, yes, I'll do it." Mom's long fingers rubbed across the bridge of her nose in small jumps.

"It's the Dutch Gap!" Alison yelled from behind the binocu-lars. "The Dutch Gap!"

The three of us stopped for one punctuated second and looked at each other. It went against years of working together as a family on the bay for us to make a decision without Dad. But on the water ahead, we could see the ripples from the splashes of the freighter's aft discharge.

"This, ahem, is the tug Pennsbury calling the Dutch Gap! Please come back."

We stared at the light blue tug. One second stretched into two seconds until five seconds mercifully ended, just for the captain to reach back to his radio mike.

"Roger, Pennsbury! This is the Dutch Gap." Alison and I shouted and jumped into the air. "How 'bout we give ya'll a little push, Miss Debbie?"

"My goodness, Dutch Gap. We would appreciate it very much, captain."

The Dutch Gap was already picking up steam as Mom released the mike button. The captain nestled his tug's pushing arms gently against our deep barge. The side wake of the barge left a giant carpet of smooth bubbles as we watched the horizon slip from catastrophe to the open channel. When the Dutch Gap slowed, the freighter was behind us, abaft our starboard beam.

"We think you're okay now, Miss Debbie," the voice in the radio bank said.

Mom nodded her head and laughed. "Goodness gracious! I do, too, captain. Thank you so very much."

As our hero tugboat pulled away from our barge, vibrations spread through our feet from the Pennsbury's decks. Our stack raced in charging gray plumes. The wheelhouse was noisy with happy shouts when Dad's greasy forearms crossed the windowsill with a loud thud.

"By God, Debbie! I never could understand that pirate stock!" Dad laughed from the wheelhouse landing. "Can you believe it? When he showed me the fuel transfer valve between the tanks, he left the #$%& valve closed! Woman, gimme that wheel!"

...   .

Suza came aboard in the coming winter of severe ice. Home

from boarding school in my senior year, I was reassigned from the galley to engine rounds on my old twelve-six watch.

Our loving Toto died at sea this winter. She died on blankets in the captain's cabin surrounded by Mom and Dad. In Toto's last gesture before she laid down her head to sleep, she licked Mom's and Dad's hands as they held her furry head. The crew buried Toto at the farm after the Pennsbury made port. They buried her beside Mom's favorite tree in open view of the family kitchen windows.

Nanticoke in winter

In that winter of severe ice, the Coast Guard tried to take Dad's master's license.

The Coast Guard required vessels to travel in convoys in ice conditions, behind a breaker. Dad called the U.S.C.G. from the telephone booth at the Seaford granary and was given permission to sail down the Nanticoke River alone. Mom radioed the Coast Guard every half hour, according to their instructions, until they got tired of her and told her not to call anymore. Pennsbury emerged from hours of grinding ice to the other side of Bloodsworth Island, where the expected convoy wasn't there. Mom and Dad continued down the bay with their load of grain.

The Coast Guard later charged that Dad had sailed without permission. Paperwork and tempers flew, but Dad's license was left intact after the hearing.

In the spring, Mom and Dad returned to the Humane Society to adopt another abandoned puppy. Their new dog was a loving moppet they named Annie.

My parents had also renamed our tug to the Nanticoke, and continued to enjoy a roster of capable crew. Todd was still aboard as sereng, with Mark and Winn, as well as a swaggering six foot Vermont farm boy named Matthew. Jono was from coastal New England. He was gifted in carpentry and small boat-handling. Young Jono, with thick black hair, would expertly assist in turning our barges at the head of the Nanticoke River with our small Boston Whaler.

"Annie" on the upper deck

Besides minor scrapes with the local roosters in our home port, the boys did try to stay out of trouble. Working three weeks on and only one week off, blowing off steam in port was natural. Usually it was jolly.

Todd did not look jolly stepping up to the dock one Sunday morning in Seaford.

The generator hummed up the deck. The granary was empty. In a rare respite, Mom and Dad had also taken the pick-up truck to the farmhouse for the night.

Jono, farthest aft, and another crewman secure the hawser board

I tossed a handful of egg shells into the current beneath the dock and shielded my eyes from the sun.

"What's up, Todd?"

"Just cook for you and Jono."

"Just two? Isn't everybody hungry?"

"Two bunks are empty."

"Empty?"

Todd set a heavy foot on the dock. "I'm walking into town," he said. "I don't know Seaford very well, but I'm bound to find a hospital and a jail. They'll be in one of 'em."

They were not at the hospital.

"You sure are lucky Frank's not here," Todd was saying several hours later as he hopped down to the foot rail. Two of our wilted, unshaven crew stood on the dock.

Author, Alison, and "Annie" tour on the stern

One spread out his hands. "But there was this girl -"

"Uhh," the other groaned and rubbed his eyes. "Why'd you let me fall asleep in the ditch like that.."

"'N she took us to this dance hall 'n we ran out of money 'n"

"Uhh!" the other groaned again. "Why'd you have'ta call that state trooper a fat bastard.."

"You sure are lucky Frank's not here," repeated Todd a little unnecessarily. "Well, get something to eat and come to the engine room. It's a short job on the battery bank. You sure are lucky."

It was Frank himself who made bail for two more of our crew a couple of weeks later in Norfolk. He put on a shore shirt and yelled to Mom, "Where's my wallet, Debbie?" One of the boys had been pushing the other in a shopping cart, and they were running from the police at the same time.

The boys, however, were protective of the captain's daughters ashore. They would line up my sisters and me on the sidewalk, and make us walk backwards into their favorite waterfront pizza place that was also a strip club.

We emptied from cabs into hand-clapping square dance halls and charging clubs with live bands blasting songs by Pablo Cruz and James Brown. They were cool with air-conditioning and crowded with the world. German, Spanish, and English seamen fell to the rhythm with high, circling bottles of cold beer. American Navy boys roared in all corners, and among the boisterous crowds, ladies of the night circulated coquettishly, with cat-like winks.

Pushing our barge beneath the Chesapeake Bay Bridges spans

With all the glitter of city ports, we enjoyed the rural pulse of our homeport. We could walk anywhere from the docks, to the movies or library. Matthew and another crewman were arrested on a Seaford street, however, for having no identification. With their threatening builds and unfamiliar faces, the police didn't take a liking to them. True, the boys would have kept the local police force more busy if all were known. But I don't think Winn got that train locomotive going too fast on that midnight spin down the granary tracks.

Jono tightens the starboad pushing cable

At night in Seaford, when tug Nanticoke could occasionally enjoy a well-deserved rest, the river banks made great echo chambers for singing. Matthew often led us in his favorite song:

"My father was the keeper of the Eddystone Light!
And he slept with a mermaid one fine night.
And from this union, there came thrrree!
The porpoise!
The porgy!
The other was me!
Hooo, hooo, the wind blows frrree!"

...   .

I turned on the granary dock in Norfolk. Frowning, I took Mom's arm. Lines of tractor trailers revved and braked behind us. Grain poured into their beds in deep and slow thunder. It was a typical backdrop to our mother-daughter talks.

"Mama?" I shouted to be heard. "I don't want to go to college!"

"What?!" Her eyes widened.

"I already got straight A's in Latin!"

"What?!"

"I want to start my own company, maybe in transportation!" I pointed to the trucks behind us. "It'd be exciting!"

We walked on. Mom clasped her temples in apparent agony. "Absolutely not!" she answered firmly, and dropped her arms as if they were weak. She resumed her normal voice as we started down the dock and away from the activity of the silos. "You are going to college, Emily."

The grain dust puffed up between our toes on the dock. We brushed the flies from our legs with second nature. "But, Mama," I implored her. "I'd be so good at it! And I can teach myself, from books!" I didn't want to go ashore to more airless classrooms.

Mom gave me a narrowed glance. I knew I would not approach my father on the subject. I was also standing with my duffle, on the same dock, two weeks later. I was off to get my degree in nursing, the wheelhouse vote, uncontested by my brave smile and slight disbelief.

Mom smiled. "My baby's going to college."

"I'll call a cab," Dad said.

I kissed Mom on the cheek and followed Dad into the granary.

After he finished at a pay phone, Dad waved me over to him. Trying to be affectionate and tenderly hold up my head, Dad's big hands only squeezed my face so I looked like a fish. His calluses scratched my sunburnt cheeks as he said, "Your Mama and I love you, do you know that?"

I nodded with my fish lips. "Yeshp." Then I suddenly wrapped my arms around his sweaty, stained shirt.

Dad looked down through his bifocals uncomfortably. "Now, now," he growled. "Let's not have any of that silly stuff. It's only college. See?" He took one of my braids in either hand and gently yanked one, and then the other, saying, "Col-lege, col-lege. Your Mama and I both went." He looked up, walking to the arriving cab. "Now it's your turn, little girl."

The Nanticoke was hidden by dockside tangles of chutes and

42

cables behind me. I twisted on the backseat of the cab and waved at her lost shape.

"I love you," I mouthed softly, under the thunder of pouring grain.

···　　　···　　　···　　　···　　　···

My bus and train ticket stubs sat on one of the two empty desks in the room. I flattened out the crumpled balls with vague thoughts of tax deductibility for an employee in travel. I sighed, and returned to one of the two bare beds. I sat between my suitcase, one that I had picked up at the farmhouse, and my typewriter case. I wrinkled my nose at the white, cinderblock walls.

More school housing except here, on the seventh floor of one of the campus dormitories, I had a view of upstate New York.

I walked across to the window and looked down on the campus road. U-hauls and family station wagons and an occasional limousine vied for space in a stretched out cloud of shouts and chaos at the small private college. Trunks filled the lawn paths. Fathers looked uncomfortable, mothers organized, and girls, everywhere, looked around excitedly at their first battle ground of freedom.

I pulled myself from the window, thoroughly homesick for the waterfront. The other girls had brought trunks, televisions, stuffed animals, and Stuff. I opened my two cases. The typewriter was the pride of my life, a blue manual Olivetti. Mom and Dad had given it to me for making honor roll my senior year at Westtown. In the suitcase was a pillow, a blanket, linens, and some changes of clothes. And a tin of snuff, its top rusted from sea air.

···　　　···　　　···　　　···　　　···

"Ohhhhh, shit!" Philip cried.

My head flew up from my pillow and my forehead hit the board slat under Alison's upper bunk. I grabbed my stinging head and yelled, "He's goin' over the rail, Al!"

43

"Philip!" Alison screamed from her bunk. "Hold on!"

Home for Thanksgiving break from our different schools, Alison and I half-sat on our rolling bunks and stared in horror at our burst open fo'c'sle door. Philip, a young muscular crewman from Virginia and my godfather's son, was holding onto the open door with one hand. His other arm was flailing in big loops behind him in the deck lights. Our Nanticoke was rolling down violently. Philip's thighs had vanished in deck wash. His surprised cry pierced the gale winds and the frenzied thudding of spray against the steel house.

I felt more than saw Nanticoke's rail rise. As the water receded around him on the deck, Philip panted and leaned through the doorway. "Em'ly," he gasped anticlimactically. "It's- it's yo' watch..." and he stumbled away.

"Ohh..." Alison groaned as the tug reeled down again. Sea spray lashed against the dogged door. "I think I'm gonna throw up."

I tumbled out of bed with the downward lurch. Cold water seeped into my shoes. "Oh! Oh!" I whimpered as goose bumps crawled up my legs. Looking back and forth over the dark floor for answers, I spotted green phosphorescence slipping about the small corner floor drain. Jelly fish were sliding in and out from the deck. "Damn. Floor's swamped."

I slid my hand down the rail of Alison's upper bunk and reached out to feel for the sink. Alison had gotten off watch early from sea sickness, and her knees were braced for balance against the wooden bunk frame, as I had just done in my bunk, to keep from rolling out.

"I hate rough weather," Alison mumbled from her pillow, "more than anythin' in th'world."

"I gotta turn the light on."

"Uh, I hate you, too."

The cold sink light cut into the room. I rubbed my eyes as Alison buried a groan into her pillow.

There was something glistening in the light, on the shelf below the porthole. I took a sloshing step toward it. I squinted sleeply at the shelf before I cried out, "Oh, no! The porthole wasn't dogged all the way!" In the pile of my science books under the dripping porthole, my thick anatomy book bulged with sea water. "Oh, no!" I whined with red, puffy eyes. "My notes! My notes! My notes! About the renal system! About urine!" I swayed with dismay in the Nanticoke's next deep roll, envisioning my professor's frown whether I had been in a sea gale or not. "I was supposed to mem'rize all about urine! Oh, God! The urine exam's next week!"

"Eeeeee!" Alison wailed. I looked up at her suffering face. "Now I know I'm gonna throw up! Go on watch, g'dammit! Please! Please!" she sobbed and pulled her pillow over her head.

…   …   …   …   …

Diesel mixed with the taste of coffee in my throat in the engine room. My eardrums rang and the shiny floor slanted away under my shoes. It was time for another engine round every thirty minutes. Our faithful engineer and bay "grandfather", Cornbread, visited often, but Dad needed an early heads-up if something was wrong down below.

Frank and our friend, Cornbread, talk things over

I circled the fiery engine in dial-reading routine. Within minutes, sweat trickled through my hair and into my eyes as I

45

stabbed a pen at the giant log tablet: M/T NANTICOKE, Lambert Tug Co. Time Record.

We did engine rounds every half hour on the "Nanticoke"

Pausing for balance in the seas, I filled the empty slots on the page with my findings: Time, 0200; Engine RPMS, 740; Eng. Oil Press. (pressure) UHd, 55; Fuel Oil Pres. In/Out, 28/9; Fresh Water Press., 34; Fresh Water Temp. In/Out, 145/149; Raw Wtr. Press., 17; Lube Temp In/Out, 156/173; Piston Oil Press., 57; Red. (reduction) Gear Oil Press., 118; Clutch Air Press., 121; A.C., 120; D.C., 128; Exhaust Temp, 710.

I left the tablet and pen on a forward table by the fuel tanks. Gingerly stepping aft, I dropped my knees to the warm deck plates and poked a broom handle deep into the bilge water to measure depth. My round complete, I cautiously rode the merry-go-round ladder to up above.

The waves tumbled and sluiced down our decks. With my hands sliding tightly along the rail, I stepped aft to check the hawser board. It smacked down rhythmically against our stern rail. Invisible beyond our deck lights, the hawser jerked away into the pitch-black.

The lashings for our deck line coils floated and twisted in the deck wash. I reached down and checked that they were fast. Foam from the seas fluttered in dirty-white against the line coils and my

46

jeans. Our American flag whipped and snapped hectically over my head. I hurried back to the galley with the gale singing in my face.

"Emmo?"

Mom and "Annie"

The galley intercom dove into my thoughts. As much as I loved Mom, I cursed under my breath. I knew I'd have to go right back on deck.

I stood from my drowned pile of science books on the galley table. "Ma?" I answered the intercom, stepping over a rolling can of evaporated milk. "Yes, Ma?"

"Oh, Emmo! How nice to hear your voice!"

My eyes clouded with affection. Mom didn't want me out in the gale either.

"Mama, can I get you something?"

"Why, yes, love. Maybe some coffee, and how about a sandwich?"

"Roger, Deb! Right away," I answered.

Inside from the whipping spray, Mom stood braced at the radar in the wheelhouse. I shut the wheelhouse door behind me, and the closed door muffled the high shrieking of the gusts. The wheelhouse was warm. Soft music played from the aft shelf.

"Not roast beef! Marvelous!"

"Your stomach okay, Debbie?" I asked.

"Yes, love. I'm fine."

"Tug Carvel, WF5513!" interrupted the radio. "Callin' the sou'bound tug 'n tow, one mile sou' Rapp'hannock Channel! Come in, cap'!"

"Emmo, hold that coffee a sec'. I have to answer Captain Yogi. Roger, Yogi!" she said into the mike. "This is the Nanticoke, WX8912, a mile south of the channel!"

"Well, hey they'a, Miss Debbie! How'a you? Might breezy out heya tonight! Come back!"

"My goodness, yes, Captain Yogi. It surely is. But Emily just brought me some hot coffee, so we should be just fine, over."

"Sound' right good, Miss Debbie! But now, I done heard 'bout yo' coffee!" Captain Yogi's laughter was interrupted by a crackle and bark on the radio, as if his mike had hit something.

Mom's silhouette was suddenly crouching for balance against the radar column in a ten foot swell. The Nanticoke rode up the mountain. I grabbed the window sill, but like someone had picked up my knees from under me, my back slammed into the sill as we dove down from the crest. Half of Mom's coffee soaked the chest of my parka, and steamed up.

"Carvel to the Nanticoke!"

"Yes, yes, roger, Captain Yogi!" Mom answered, braced over the compass.

"You gettin' these good sized waves ov'a they'a? Ov'a!"

Mom whispered, with her thumb off the mike button, "Damn it!" Mom rarely swore. "I've never had a harder time holding 210. It's the incoming tide fighting the wind, making these waves so big." Mom was beginning to sound scared. I frowned at the cascading wave tops coming and coming into our deck lights.

Mom cleared her throat, "Yes, Yogi, it's got to be this tide," she said calmly into the mike. "I see we'll be passing port to port. One whistle. Over."

"A one whistle passin' is just fine, Miss Debbie! You have a good night now, hey'a? You be careful now, Miss Debbie! Carvel out."

"Thank you, and roger, Carvel. Good sailing. Nanticoke out."

The binocular strap stood out, and then slapped the bulkhead, as we rose and then heeled down again. I was frowning at the waves, and listening for the strap to fall, when Mom's light voice crossed the slanting deck. "Dearie? Any of that coffee left?"

My love showered for her.

Suza stands next to our ice-damaged prop in the spring

At the end of our watch, Mom leaned out the wheelhouse window. "Take my pinky! Go ahead, take my pinky and squeeze!"

"Mama!" I chuckled on the landing.

The dawn was a boiling concoction of gold and gray behind my shoulders. Wind had dropped to ten knots, a settling breeze to Mom and me after our midnight watch. The six hours had left soft, dark smudges under our eyes, and from our exhaustion, we were no less light-headed than helium.

I shifted Mom's breakfast plate of scrapple, eggs, toast, jam, and cottage cheese, with a green sprig. Of something. I reached through the window and squeezed Mom's pinky.

"A-ha!" Mom bubbled. "I'll have to change my name to Gretel, and you're the forest witch, love! Fattening me up for the oven!" Laughing, I passed Mom's plate over the salt-crusted pane as she patted her chest and sighed, "How delicious, dear chef! Oh, guess what? You're not going to believe it!"

With red eyes, I spat some tobacco off the landing and leaned back into the window. "What, Ma?"

"When you were doing your last engine round, 'Row, Row, Row Your Boat' came over the F.M. station! And I played it!"

"Ma!"

"Over channel thirteen! I held the mike up to the radio!"

We swayed giggling over her F.C.C. secret.

"Hey, woman..." Dad's deep, sleepy voice filled the wheelhouse as he climbed stiffly from the captain's cabin. "How goes it..."

"Good morning, Bood!" Mom turned brightly. She balanced her plate on an aft shelf and slipped her arms around Dad's big stomach.

"Knock that off, woman. You're giddy."

"I love you, Bood."

"I love you, too, woman. But not after you've been on watch for six hours."

With Mom and our first mascot, devoted "Toto"

At this, Mom's and my laughter built on itself until we were trying to catch our breath. We wiped the tears from our eyes as Dad looked back and forth between us suspiciously. "If you girls weren't so damn dumb, you'd worry me." And Mom's and my knees folded under us. "Good God, you women. Never have I seen a sillier bunch on a tugboat! Little Emily, bring your father some coffee without falling overside from that giddy stuff."

I skipped laughing down below to the galley. "Good morning, everybody!" Murderous eyes glanced up from a hunched row of gray faces. "Isn't the dawn loverly?"

Dutifully toting along the water-stained pages of my anatomy book for summer study, I returned to the tug in early June.

Crewman Philip passes on Red Bandana Day! Unless we were making port, we couldn't receive t.v. or radio music signals on the water, and entertained ourselves.

It was decided that Alison was old enough to share an apartment at the beach with friends. With a cherished pile of love letters carefully tucked away in my fo'c'sle, from my North Carolina beau, Don, I returned home to the tug Naticoke. I was eighteen.

Alison and "Annie"

...   .

A year of intense science study was behind me. My crew now became specimens for my summer laboratory!

Mom didn't just have a stuffy nose. She had released histamines in her upper respiratory passage. And they formed antibodies that destroyed allergens. And the released histamine increased the permeability of blood vessels. That caused edema. Or swelling. Or a stuffy nose.

And Jono didn't just cut his hand on the barge rail. The cut entered his epidermis into the subcutaneous. And the bleeding from the capillaries was slowed by coagulation, in calcium interacting with platelet breakdown into thromboplastin...

The crew loved it. They loved me after my first year of college. Well, maybe they did.

"Mom! Dad!" I sang from the stern as I cleaned a bucket of fish in Englehard, North Carolina. "Mom! Dad!" They were walking forward. "Frank! Debbie!"

"What is it?" They turned around on the deck.

"Isn't this fish great? Look at the eyeball!" I pinched my fingers into the fish's eye. A little glass ball glinted in the ooze. "The lens!" I said triumphantly.

"Ohh.." Mom grimaced.

"That's fascinating, Emily," Dad answered stoically.

"And, look! This is the digestive track. See how it's protected in the cartilage? Let me show you the stomach."

"Emily, darling," Mom said, swallowing uncomfortably. "Aren't you quite the biologist."

I glowed with the encouragement and pointed my knife at the slime. "The neat thing is how all this stuff works, just like for people! All the systems serve the same purpose of regulation. That's called homeostasis! Hey, look at this great digestive tract!" I slit open the rest of the fish and pointed. "The excrement can be located perfectly down from the stomach!" Mom and Dad looked at the bubbly yellow guts. "That reminds me! When do you guys want supper?"

. . .　　. . .　　. . .　　. . .　　. . .

"That's called peristalsis, Ma."

"What?" Mom leaned into the binoculars. "What did you say?"

"You said you could just about go, and I said, 'That's called peristalsis.'"

Mom lowered the binoculars and pressed her finger into an old chart. The banks of the Intercoastal Waterway had diminished into faraway brown lines. We were steaming a light barge southward on the Ditch. A bridge wavered in the thick humidity ahead. It looked thin on the horizon, like a warped white toothpick.

Fog on the "Ditch"

"Emily," Mom said without looking up. "I said that taking this barge through that bridge is going to make me go in my-"

"Needless say, Ma," I said over a spate of static from the radio bank, "poopin' is called 'peristalsis'. It's the short muscle action of the long intestine-"

"Oh, God!" Mom sighed. She looked ahead at the approaching bridge. "It looks so small. I think I'm just going to die."

"Gee, Ma, diein' and poopin' are different."

"Emily.. Dear," Mom said, and flashed a frown at me. She pointed at the hazy channel. "I have to take this big, big barge through that tiny little bridge up there." I looked from Mom to the bridge. "Now put down that anatomy book, please, for just a minute. I need time to think."

I tilted my head and threw out my hands. "Ma! Debbie! You're gonna make it! The hole will get bigger!"

"My hands are shaking!"

"But that's normal! Do you know what my psychology professor always says? Dr. Stevens always says-"

"Maybe we should have let you drive a truck!"

Albermarle and Pamlico Canal on the "Ditch"

"Own trucks, Ma, and maybe that bridge has a Freudian hold on your sense of, let's see," I paused,   scratching my shoulder and leaning down to the spittoon. "Wait. That's Jung."

"Emily!"

"Mama, let's talk about it. Tell me how you feel."

"I feel like tying you to that damn beacon until I get through the bridge!"

I laughed and wrapped my arms around Mom's waist. "How about if I go to the galley and get you some iced tea instead?"

"Yes, child- Go!"

"Roger!" I sang and pivoted onto the wheelhouse landing. "Now, aren't you glad," I said seriously, frowning over the window pane, "that you sent me to college?"

The roughness of the breeze was at first a balm. Warm ocean breakers of air tossed and broke through the galley's screened doors. Our red gingham curtains billowed on the portholes. Pages from the boys' paperbacks fluttered on the table. Pens rolled away.

Our galley

The month of July had come up on the galley calendar. We were pushing a hot asphalt barge from Baltimore to South Richmond, Virginia. We had done it before, all summer it seemed: the asphalt had to be kept hot, hotter than one hundred and fifty degrees, to not sludge up at pump-off. The radiated heat from the two hundred foot barge at our pushing puddin was an inferno in our lungs.

The bargeman who monitored cargo temperature and maintained the vessel's engines was a middle-aged man with a nice disposition. Bob lived on our tug while we transported Hot Oil 17. But our routines and even our language aboard were, by the end of each trip, reduced to near mind-reading. Onboard fatigue was constant. Nobody slept well off-watch. Fumes from Hot Oil 17's deck engine shack poured black soot in a steady column onto our powering tug Nanticoke. We mostly pushed Hot Oil 17, begrudging as we were to take the time and labor to put the barge on the string in calm weather.

Author on deck

En route to South Richmond, we would steam pass the spectacular Naval ghost fleet on the James River. There was little pleasure ahead otherwise, up the narrow, airless head of the James. It would become 110 degrees in the galley tied to Hot Oil 17. It was hot.

So the baths of wind coursing through the boat and blowing away the barge's soot felt like a generous reprieve. The Atlantic met the Chesapeake a dozen miles off our port. The water was leaping in a chop as far as the eye could see.

But the soothing wind started gusting too hard. Thick green waves bellied up to three feet. Our pushing cables started singing out in protest from the strain. It was time to break pushing and tow. The galley intercom barked out something to this effect, and my cooking was interrupted in routine. Without a second thought, I shoved two heavy frying pans of beef liver to the back of the stove, with all the lightning of onions in the pans, and scurried aft from my windswept galley.

"Annie" in the stern

"Break port winch?" I shouted.

Mark nodded quickly in the wind. We stepped to the port winch wheel. Grunting with planted feet, we hauled down on the wheel together. We hurried to free the tooth brake or dog.

The wheel spun out free. Its spokes were a blur at fifty to sixty revolutions per second. In a fraction of those seconds, a running bull of a swell punched our stern and the winch wheel was spinning out with me in it. The violent beating was over as quickly as it started and I was looking at the sky.

Clouds can be as blinding as sunshine.

I tried to lift my right hand to shield my eyes. Pain riveted up my hand when I touched it to my face. I looked at my hand, and like an alien thing before my eyes, my thumb was swelling into the size of a tennis ball. I had landed my full weight on my thumb on the deck, before slamming onto my back, thrown like a rag doll against the sharp, steel rim of the hawser table. Still, I was sensing a different kind of pain. I searched Mark's shocked face. Then I joined his stare at my lap.

The skin on my pelvis, hip, and thigh was missing, replaced by raw purple. I groped at the bloody, remaining threads of my shorts and underwear to cover myself. I was exposed.

The voices were in a tunnel, shouting, where Dad's big frame was trembling on the upper deck. The boys and Bob were running onto the stern deck, as if into a wall when they saw me. Then there was Mom's scream, as she ran onto the stern and into the invisible net. Her eyes ran wildly over the deck and found me.

I cried for a towel or a blanket, with the idea of holding it all in. I was helped up the deck, over the coaming, onto my bunk.

I flattened out on my stomach, crying out. My pelvis felt crushed. The raw flesh was swelling outward, bulging out, from internal bleeding. My mind started slowly spiraling in black and gray as my bunk rose up, and plunged down, again and again, in the sparkling summer seas.

I wouldn't stop begging for water. It was frightening Mom.

"I-I.." she started. "Papa's on the radio to the Coast Guard." The screened door opened and shut. I drew a shaky hand to my face. My fo'c'sle bunk lunged down in another sea trough, and I gasped into my swollen fingers.

"The medic on the Coast Guard boat says no water, Emily." Mom's voice returned with more control in it. I felt her sit on the narrow mattress. She ducked her head under the upper bunk. "He says to... oh, Emily." Her voice was a whisper. "It is bad." She cleared her throat. "I have to peel off your shorts and panties now," and a claw hoe sank into my back.

"No, no," I protested.

"Oh, Emily. Look!"

I twisted my head and then dropped it, trying to breathe. A purple swelling of blood, the size of half a soccer ball, was bulging out from the internal bleeding. It was rolling and shining over my right hip, buttock, and down the back of my leg to mid-thigh. My shorts and panties were shredded and tangled into it. Dirt and rust chips from the deck were embedded into it. I squeezed my eyes and clutched the wooden frame of my bunk with my good hand, until my hand shook, as Mom pulled out the threads and the debris.

An hour passed. I could feel that the chop of the seas was lessening. I was grateful that my bunk stopped lunging.

I continued to lay on my bunk, now so thirsty from blood loss that my tongue felt like an expanding, blocking cork in my throat. Mom was coming and going tensely to report to the wheelhouse. Dad had briskly stepped into my fo'c'sle, too devastated to speak, and continued radioing the Coast Guard vessel en route with medics. Mom brought their instructions to my fo'c'sle. She removed foreign material from the wound, denied me water, and wrapped my lower, naked body in a sheet. Each decision took long minutes in between. An hour and a half passed. Mom was brushing my hair into a braid down the side.

"People ashore.." I tried to swallow but couldn't. "Water.." my voice rattled. "Coas' Guard.. Don' let them see me naked, Mama.."

"Hush, darling." The restrained roar of our engine at slow ahead made the passing hush of the seas seem clearer through the fo'c'sle door. "There now," Mom said softly, and it was quiet again. She finished wrapping the rubber band at the bottom of my braid. "Mark will be with you," she started to say, and took a deep breath. "I have to stay aboard with the Coast Guard coming, for two licenses aboard.. We can't stop with the asphalt or it will cool. We'll destroy the cargo to stop."

"Ma. I know that.. I know.."

"Mark's ready to go ashore with you." She stood from the bunk and stepped to the screened door. Her eyes were sad. Her mouth was pulled back. "I see the Coast Guard vessel now."

The wind moaned through the doorway but it didn't ruffle Mom's red checked shirt, or her brunette pony tail. My eyes rolled up to receive her kiss on my forehead. She was streaming with sweat.

"Starboard side!" I could hear Dad shouting.

A crash sounded from our rail. The Nanticoke shuddered. A powerful engine roared and died, and roared again to another crash.

"This is it, Emily."

"Mama?"

"She's in here!" Jono was yelling on deck. "Here! Here!"

The screened door banged open. Mom was pressed back against the lockers as strangers in white shirts straddled the coaming and crowded into my fo'c'sle.

"Stretcha'! Blanket!" One of the men dashed back on deck as a soft hand spread over my sunburnt cheeks and pushed up an eyelid. "Victim is in shock! Radio ashore, immedite I.V., severe trauma, lower body! Now get her the hell aboard!"

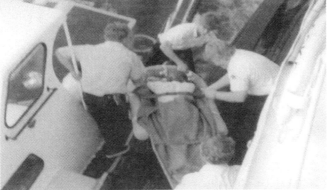

USCG rescue

61

USCG rescue

The strangers transferred me onto a stretcher under a heavy wool blanket. The stretcher tilted through the air. My crew and the Coast Guard men handed it across the rails and it landed with a thud onto the rescue vessel, the engine already roaring. I buried my chin into my shoulder to see behind me. Mark made a leap onto the vessel's stern. Its propeller sang with air before the stern dug down, and ground into the seas for Norfolk.

The Nanticoke was pulling away. Her shiny black bow was cutting into the green seas. I thought I saw Mom, standing on the deck, but I clenched my eyes against the brightness.

···   ···   ···   ···   ···

The engine held a high-pitched scream as we jarred into the waves for the hour and a half to Norfolk. With brilliant blue eyes, a handsome medic stood by reading my pulse with the bow spray fanning up and whispering behind him. My simple female awareness of his eyes kept me from slipping into madness from pain on the small, screaming boat.

The engine quieted. My stretcher became airborne again, onto a trolley that thudded down dock planks like a finger down a scrub board. After traveling at six knots for six weeks, I was suddenly in an ambulance hurtling at seventy miles an hour with a noontime dry dock whistle on its roof that wouldn't shut off.

In the ambulance, the medic packed ice over me with Latex surgical gloves that had been filled with water and frozen. Condensation was forming on the gloves from the heat, I saw, with greedy eyes. I gazed up. "C-can I.. lick a finger? Plee'.. plee'.."

Mark, weaving on the floor of the ambulance with its speedy turns, looked up. The medic looked at both of us, and nodded reluctantly. "A little."

I flopped a hand over the glove and pulled it to my mouth. I ran a tongue down a frozen finger. My eyes slid shut. I had made peace with all the world and wanted to drift away to sleep.

"You're gonna be awright, hon'," a blonde-haired nurse was saying out of breath as the emergency room walls blurred by. We jarred to a stop in a cubicle. Like a magic act, intravenous equipment flew through her fingers and found my arm.

"Not.." I tried to say, " ..good arm.."

"This other arm's hurt, hon'," she was saying as a needle sliced into my forearm. She pressed white tape over the needle. A clink of the I.V. pole, and the nurse was on my other side, talking to the medic in low tones.

"Okay, how do you do," a man with dark eyes asked in a statement at the end of my bed. I stared at him with glazed eyes. The curtain was still swaying from his entrance. "I'm Dr. Gallo. Let's take a look." He held up the sheet like a tent and looked underneath.

Technical words and abbreviations tossed back and forth between the mustached Italian doctor and the medic until a tall, striking Arab strode briskly into the cubicle from the curtains. My sheet was whisked fully off with authority.

"I am Dr. Jarali," the Arab said to no one in particular. He ran his eyes over a clipboard and fell on my body with quick fingers. "Never, never have I zeen so much trauma!" he cried suddenly. "Not zince the war! Look at thiz hematoma! Never have I zeen such a large hematoma! And look!" he exclaimed. I lifted my head. Dr. Jarali had swept his arms into the air, holding up a red alga-like clump with a pair of tweezers. "Muscle!" he cried.

"Muscle?" I sobbed to Dr. Gallo. My eyes searched his face, for confirmation that I'd be lame. My head fell to the pillow.

"No, it's coagulated blood, miss. He's just excited."

"Muscle! Muscle!" Dr. Jarali delighted. "Now!" he orchestrated suddenly, and as he spoke, the staff rushed in different directions. "Very good," he was saying. "We will be draining this hematoma as zoon as possible." I could feel his fingers as he spoke, horridly over the open wounds. "What iz this?" the doctor demanded at my feet. He pointed a finger at my soles. "Look at theeze black feet! Young leedy, where have you been?"

"A tugboat girl, doc," the medic was saying as he pulled back a curtain. "I got you a pretty little tugboat girl." He smiled over to me before vanishing through the curtains. I grabbed my eyes to see him go, the person who had brought me here to land, the person who understood where I came from. The I.V. yanked back my arm, and the flat, white walls swam.

"We have to drain this blood, miss." Dr. Gallo said with a hand on my trembling shoulder.

"I know," my voice cracked. "The doctor with my muscle said that. My name," I added, "is Em'ly." Moisture was beginning to lace my mouth.

"And then we're taking you to x-ray-"

"Oh, my-"

" -to see if anything's broken."

"I can't tell," I whispered sadly.

"Dr. Jarali, this is Emily," continued Dr. Gallo.

"Amily! This iz a wonderful name!" Dr. Jarali's and my eyes met. "Such black feet you have, Amily!" he laughed as he posed over my hip with a needle the size of the pyramids.

I thought of the fish in the Englehard cleaning houses. I was packed in ice, in a line of trolleys in the emergency room hallway, waiting for a room with that night's gunshot and heart attack victims of the city of Norfolk. It was late. My kind godfather Heath had checked on me and left, taking a very tired Mark with him.

I laid face down in the ice packing, propped up at an angle on my left hip. The hematoma blood had been released in a slow spray. The x-ray showed nothing broken in the pelvic area. To assess muscle damage, I was asked to do some range of motion with my right leg. This exposed my private area to several emergency room personnel crowded inside the cubicle, and my mind whirled with teenage shame. As I laid in the hallway in the ice, I squeezed my eyes shut from the devastating memory of it.

I was heavily drugged when Mom walked down the poverty ward and found my bed the next day. The internal bleeding flowed, and pressure against the bandages was unendurable. I tossed in my bed like a slow, broken washing machine.

"Can't you.." I heard Mom's light voice say.

A nurse answered, "Our orders are to not touch the bandages."

"But she's in such pain. Look at her."

"Please," I shivered. "Please loosen them."

The nurse hesitated, and then bent to my side. The pressure eased and my tossing stopped.

"Try to eat, Emmo," Mom urged. Trays of warm puddings and beets and cellophane-wrapped crackers were being passed out on the crowded ward. The smell of body odor and urine wafted in the air. Moans floated up here and there from the dozen filled beds. With half-closed eyes, I looked down from the cracked plaster on the far wall to Mom's worried face.

"You go 'head, Ma," I whispered.

"Do try," she persisted.

I felt guilty not to, looking into her worried eyes. I slowly took up some crackers and could only fumble with the cellophane pathetically. Frustrated tears came to my eyes.

Mom took the crackers from my swollen fingers and opened them, with a tender smile, and opened a container of milk. "Try to drink it.."

She disappeared from me in a haze.

"Wh-what?" I murmured at a white uniform. A nurse materialized by my bed. The ward was quiet. Beside the nurse was the

Arab doctor.

"Look at the state of theeze bandages!"

"She begged to have them loosened, doctor. She was in a lot of pain."

I blinked at Dr. Jarali, adjusting my eyes. "Amily," he said, busying his hands at my side. "How are you?"

"No, no," I protested weakly as my body was turned.

"We redo theeze and you will be all right, yes?"

I dug my bruised fingers into the pillow. I clenched my eyes, my stomach too empty to vomit. Dr. Jarali worked without hesitation and was soon gone. The nurse injected a syringe into the I.V. tubing. "For the pain." She turned away.

"Why.." I whispered to her back, "does my back hurt when I move?"

"Honey, you're cut up pretty good back there."

I stared, trying to focus on the foggy silhouette of her face. The ward was cool and dark.

"Anything else?"

I shook my head slowly, blinking back tears, and slipped back into unconsciousness.

I was transferred to a modern hospital wing a few days later. Already fifteen pounds lighter, I was taken to physical therapy with the hope of getting me back home quickly. I was black and blue with thick scabs from my waist to mid-thigh. My limbs were bruised and they shook, but I took five steps in therapy. This ruptured open all the internal bleeding in my hip and thigh again.

"What iz this, Amily?"

Dr. Jarali stood with a tall, blonde doctor over my mid-section. I twisted in my bed to watch their faces.

The blonde doctor pulled a pencil from his white lab coat. He tapped a saucer-sized scab. The pencil eraser made a deep hollow noise. Heavy swelling was evident around the thick, caked blood.

Dr. Jarali returned from their hall conference alone. He sat on the edge of my bed. "Dr. Peabody iz a plastic surgeon. He does not think there iz anything under our scabs." He looked a little crestfallen. "So, Amily," he sighed, "thiz means we have to operate. You are still bleeding inside, you see, and when our scabs fall off, there will be nothing there. So it must be cut away, all this flesh that cannot heal. We must cut down to the good flesh."

I stared at him, unable to organize his words in my head, unable to take a full breath. These shore people were going to cut me open here.

Surgery.

"Surgery?" I whispered.

Dr. Jarali nodded.

I dropped my head back to my pillow. My heart was thumping. The white walls took a step closer. I could see the seas climbing, the winch wheel spinning, and I was falling again far, far from my world.

For the next couple of weeks, I was propped on my left side in the gray world of pain. Surgery had left drainage tubes leading out of thick hip bandages, as well as the mystery of what was or wasn't underneath. Internal bleeding continued from the damaged capillaries inside my leg.

The next attempted surgery couldn't sew or improve what were deep, wide holes from the first. Dr. Peabody came into my room and pulled out the implanted tubes without anesthesia, because so few nerves were left. I watched as he filled a four-inch wide hole with gauze, one inch deep.

"It was like sewing cheese," the surgeon blandly explained as he worked.

"But the holes," I replied hoarsely, brushing away my tears of disappointment.

"The consequent procedure," the doctor continued, referring to his clipboard, "will include changing the dressing every four hours. This will enhance tissue granulation, by pulling off the remaining dead cells. Granulation is the process of healing." He raised his light eyebrows for my acknowledgement. I nodded with resignation, and he scurried into the hall opening another chart.

"No!" I hissed with tight fists.

On the darkened side of the hospital room, my elderly roommate stirred. "Patty?" she asked no one.

The night shift nurse sighed at my roommate and then at me. "It's gotta come off, honey. You know the routine." Her red-painted fingernails, aiming again toward my hip, glittered in the bed light. She started pulling out the imbedded squares of gauze. Exposed to the air, existing nerve endings clung to the gauze. My eyelids trembled from being squeezed shut, and I cracked them open when I thought the nurse had finished. There were just no nerves left in some of the holes. She taped on fresh dressing with all the new gauze.

After two days of this procedure several times a day, I removed the gauze from the raw holes myself. It was the only way I could manage it.

Like Babe recovering from a deep, broadside swell, I rolled back from the second operation. I wanted to wash myself. My feet were still black and my hair was still heavy with salt from bucket showers on the stern. I asked a nurse about my hair, and she arranged to have me wheeled on a trolley into a supply room. She washed my hair off the end of the trolley in a janitor's sink.

I was glad to receive a letter from the tug. The crew had drawn their cartoon portraits on a folded piece of paper with a poem inside:

The house is green,
the hull is black,
the cooking is lousy,
So please come back.

Dad also sent a poem:

To You Who Has The Drain-o
Indeed the doctors are a farce

68

Unable to fix Emily's arse
With skin and drains and flesh and stuff
And still maintain their weekend off.

And Emy cares not what they say
About their lengthy Labor Day
Or how they whine and cry and shout
For Em'ly longs just to get out.

So lash the doctors with your scorn
For why they should release her morn
So she can rise and say carefree
Those doctors have been good to me!

...　　...　　...　　...　　...

Attending college in Norfolk, Philip was often at my bedside
after the operations. Out of the haze I would see his shadow, and
then the details of his handsome face framed in curly brown hair.
Godfather Heath also took the time beside my bed for unhurried
conversation. Their kind visits and others, from ex-crewmen and
my beau from North Carolina, from amorous doctors with flowers
and candy, displaced fear with optimism.

A hospital aide offered surprising support, too.

She was emptying the small, plastic waste cans from my room.
I looked up from the sloppy spread of papers and books on my
bed table and watched her familiar black hands knot a garbage bag.
She never returned my small hello's. She only reluctantly nodded.
But I turned awkwardly in my bed with my bandage hump and
watched her clean the room, glad for her company.

Between shyness and being a teenager, I couldn't articulate the
emotions climbing inside me from my violent journey. It had been
a challenge to cope with an injury in a big city hospital, in conference with a staff of doctors and changing nurses and huge aides,
rolling me onto elevators as they laughed and talked, through the
haze of shivery pain. My elderly roommate, suffering a broken hip

69

and in the throes of senility, kept calling me Patty and asking for a map of Cleveland. I hadn't yet cried in the hospital from the stress of it, and the tears quietly came all at once.

The aide stopped cleaning. She slowly walked from the cart to the window. She simply stood against the light without talking, until my quiet sobs subsided and I breathed deeply. She gave me a minute to wipe my face before she turned. Finally she smiled, and pushed her cleaning cart from the room.

Sir Author Conan Doyle did his part, too. It was when Sherlock Holmes and I were dodging together over the cold moors to Baskerville castle that I looked up from my book to a half dozen medical students filing into my room with clipboards. They leaned down in their white lab coats to my bandages like a football huddle with their foreheads pulled together over my hip.

A blush burned across my face. I brought a hand to my face, trying to control my laughter. It had been too much to catapult from my isolated maritime life and now lay ashore half-naked in front of endless medical personnel.

It was a big day when I was able to stand from my hospital bed. After fuss and discussion over the wound, the shift nurse even allowed me to take a shower. The sensation of water over my side was plainly sickening, but the end improvement to my morale was invaluable.

I was combing out my wet hair when Philip arrived with an armful of newspapers. They were copies of an article about Norfolk's rescue units and their adventures, including my rescue.

"'Cramped bunkroom'?" I quoted from a paper on my bed. "My fo'c'sle's huge! 'Tall, attractive blonde'? Well, that part was nice of the reporter. Philip? Do you think we can leave this place for a while? I want to go outside so much."

"We can try," he said, and turned for me to dress. I changed into a set of shore clothes Mom had brought optimistically on her first visit, when I was still on the poverty ward. I put on the skirt, blouse, and sandals, and extra layers of tape over my hip to hold the bandages in place.

"I'm ready!" I announced. It felt great to be in real clothes.

"But how do we get to the elevator without the station nurse seeing us?"

Philip grinned and stepped to the door. Without looking over his shoulder, he waved me over.

"Don't forget to feed the cows, Patty."

"Yes, ma'am," I said to my roommate, and crept along the nighttime corridor on Philip's arm. We paused for camouflage at a water fountain. Soon we were quietly gasping for air, our eyes rimming with tears, as we sneaked onto the elevator in the dim hallway.

The heat and humidity of the Virginia night hit like a bucket of warm water. Sweat built up on my neck and chest. The rich air whirled against my face from the open windows of Philip's car as we drove to a night spot where an ex-crewman, Mike, worked.

Philip muscled out a spot for us at the packed bar. Exchanging handshakes and happy shouts, Mike set up cold drafts. The customers were young and surging in the loud music. I clung grinning to my companion's arm, my head reeling in the sudden explosion of life.

Philip was shouting into my ear, "Are you okay?" I all at once looked like I had bitten into a lemon. Someone had bumped into my hip. I nodded perkily to Philip, though my eyes slightly swam, and I didn't resist his offer to take me back to the hospital.

The security guards wouldn't allow Philip entry because visiting hours were long over. I would have to return alone from my A.W.O.L. He waited by the glass of the emergency room doors until I was inside. I turned and mouthed "good night" and waved the flower he had brought for me. Philip smiled, and bowed his curly head, and disappeared from the glass.

··· ··· ··· ··· ···

"Amily!!"

I spun around in the emergency room hallway. I slowed the twirl of my skirt.

"Amily.." Alireza's crisp lab coat rustled as he stepped up to

me and gazed down into my eyes. "Zuch a lovely flower." I swept it
to my nose, wanting to hide behind it.

"Come!" he commanded. "Come with me!" He led me to a
brightly lit room. "I have a patient!"

"Alireza!" I protested. "I shouldn't! I snuck off ward and-"

"Do not worry," he said casually, and guided my elbow as I
limped to keep up. "You are a medical student, yes?"

"I'm a nur-"

"Sit."

Alireza pointed to a tall stool in the corner of the examination
room. Gathering my skirt around my knees, and leaning awkwardly
to my left, I sat. As I balanced on the stool, my eyes steadied on a
muscular black teenager heaped in the center of the room on a
trolley. From a tree trunk neck, his head rolled back and forth
lifelessly in Alireza's hands. A pale, sandy-haired intern worked on
the boy's temples. He was shaving the sides of the boy's head.

The teen's eyes occasionally opened and scanned the room but
showed no restlessness. I regretted infringing on his privacy and
hoped his eyes wouldn't scan over to me. I thoughtfully looked at
his face, at his oddly sparkly lips for a man, as they glistened with
ointment. Finally I remembered: ointment was applied to patients
not expected to hydrate themselves.

My text book understanding collided with reality to hear the
cracking of breaking bone as Alireza and the intern screwed bolts
into the young man's skull. They fastened a collar with a hook to
hoist his head. The metal hook slipped smoothly back and forth on
its collar. The doctors worked, and the boy's hands laid inert, palms
out, on the trolley sheets. Iodine drizzled down his beardless face
from the stainless steel screws. His bare feet were tall and still at
end of the trolley, like abandoned towers.

"Basketball game.. A fight," Alireza explained at the door. "He
was thrown, paralyzed from the neck down. Here. The family.
Good night, Amily. I must talk to them." I followed his eyes down
the hallway to a row of tired faces filling a bench.

"Good night," I whispered to his back. I watched him slow
and bend forward to the crowded bench. The expectant faces

turned up to him.

Three days later, the hospital traffic inched below my window in the hot summer sun. My things had been packed since early morning, and sat in plastic bags on my bed.

"Emily?" Tall and tan, Mom walked into the room with warm hug. A nurse pushed an empty wheelchair behind her. The papers were signed, and my doctors had released me. Granulation had started in the holes and the rest was up to time. My instructions were to change the gauze dressings twice a day with douses of saline solution.

Mom and I drove the five hours north from Norfolk to the tug in Seaford. I mostly dozed, overwhelmed by the pace and noise and heat outside the hospital.

"Emmo, be careful! Go slowly!"

I didn't answer, but smiled and stretched out a pale hand to Jono on the upper deck. I had boarded the light barge without difficulty. The barge deck had been even with the pier. But to reach the tug there was only the typical bouncing plank over a fifteen foot drop, from the barge deck to the upper deck of the tug. I reached out to Jono's callused, guiding hands.

The black stack murmured generator puffs on the upper deck in front of a raging blue sky. Jono kindly talked me across the plank. He finally just lifted me down to the upper deck, and from a world away, I was back home.

Between islands of permanent numbness on my hip, angry currents of familiar pain washed up and down my side. I descended the wheelhouse ladder with my right leg as stiff as I could hold it. Otherwise, the open flesh would fold on itself. My stomach flopped a little from that sensation when I raised my leg over the galley coaming, but I had to laugh when I saw the refrigerator. A grease-smudged note in one of the boys' handwriting read: "Lambert Tug Co Inc. expects everyone to Bust Ass on this Boat."

Their work day over, Dad and the boys were sitting on the shaded rail outside the galley. I looked out at their faces, framed by

73

the turning river, and stepped on deck.

I smiled broadly at my crew. The men greeted me and briefly smiled back, but they were somber. I was surprised. Hoisting my leg after me over the galley coaming, I felt an unexpected sadness for my good crew: it hadn't entered my mind that they might feel responsible for what had happened.

"Come back to the stern," Dad said after I hugged him. "Show me what happened."

I knew Dad well enough to understand his old-school therapy, to get back on the horse that threw you. I limped after him and the boys until I laid my eyes on the winch wheel. I turned around on the stern deck and shuffled to get back to the bow. Dad called to me. I edged astern again with a strong feeling of unease.

"Show me what happened," Dad said again. He sat down on the rail. I stepped back and forth a little, and pointed in the wheel's direction.

"I was standing there," I swallowed, my voice sounding tight, "and I guess I got thrown over there."

Dad's eyes were steady, and I understood. I knew the winch wheel could be respected without being feared.

I walked over to the winch and rested a hand on the wheel. "I was standing here," I said. "And I didn't have my proper footing." Mom and Dad and the crew seemed to relax a little when I shook my head and smiled at them. "The boat looks great," I said. I pointed to our Amercian flag on the upper deck. "Is that a new flag? It looks great." I was glad to hear some conversation come up about the flag, because I wasn't just resting myself on the winch. I was holding myself up: I saw that an iron spoke in the wheel had actually bent from its force of hitting my body.

Bent winch wheel spoke

Dad might have forced me to confront my fears, but after taking me to the farmhouse, he and Mom jumped up in the living room, nearly knocking their chairs over backwards, the first time they watched me change the hip dressing on the couch. I wondered if I was wrong to show it to them. I had gotten used to week after week of calm, unemotional hospital staff poking the fleshy gaps like crazy. I felt devastated for Mom when she cried out in a moment of despair. She held her hands to her face. I realized then how much strength and mental acceptance I had gained in the hospital of the disfiguring injury.

My sister, Liz, was posted at the farmhouse with me for a few days until Mom and Dad agreed I could rejoin the Nanticoke in Baltimore. Five weeks later I was re-hospitalized with a spiking temperature and blood sepsis. The internal bleeding had never stopped and became septic.

Alireza was as pleased as heck to see me; in a few months, he would ask me to marry him on a visit to my college. After the welding torch of infection inside my thigh was brought out with bathes and antibiotics, I was pleased to see Alireza, too.

More tubes were implanted in my thigh. They were connected to a squashed, plastic accordion called a Hemovac that drew out fluid and infection. After a week, the tubes were pulled out, again without local anesthesia, and, I was again discharged from Norfolk

General.

Ten days after my release, I was determined to try to stay on my school schedule. I told my parents I would be fine, waved goodbye as the Nanticoke sailed from Seaford, and drove the pick-up from the granary to the farm. I got my trunk of stuff, to begin my first clinical year of nursing study in New York City. I had never been to New York City. With the coaxing of fifty dollars, I got a local farm boy to go with me in order to drive the pick-up truck back to the docks.

I felt comfortable in Manhattan from the first day. But another dormitory room and another roommate waited there. A bay window generously opened over my desk to a view of East 38th Street. To my right, the Empire State Building dominated the view of the west. But my eyes were drawn with tenderness to the east, to the traffic of the East River, where tugboats navigated the powerful currents through my torn heart.

Classrooms were located on the lower floor of my building. After receiving many course syllabi, a foot deep in ardent nursing philosophy, I'd return to my room for a pinch of snuff and to change my hip dressing in familiar routine.

Except for one last hole, the rest was slowly sealing into shiny, coral-colored scars. The largest scar spread over my side as wide as an opened hand and sank inward two inches. The surrounding skin was irregular in color and feel. My thigh, almost to my knee, was hard to the touch and uneven from internal scarring, a lot from the infection. Except for an odd, electrical-biting sensation here and there, I had no working nerves, like for hot, cold, or pressure. I favored my left side in sleeping and sitting without padding on the right.

Sitting on the hard classroom chairs was uncomfortable, and there was no end to my roommate's fuming that I got nice grades despite skipping most my classes. The sunken in scar tissue, where soft flesh should have been, was rubbed continually by my upper femur bone. That part of the femur, the superior trochanter epiphysis, projected into scar tissue that shouldn't have been there. It felt like the round end of a key rubbing back and forth at one spot from the inside. The result would be lifelong ache in the upper thigh, fluctuating back and forth on a finicky daily basis from mild to acute. The clicking in the hip when I walked was audible to companions walking beside me on sidewalks. It was from debris tossed into the joint from the trauma, like bone cells that shouldn't have been there, according to a brief but kind follow-up correspondence with Dr. Peabody.

I found rest through writing. Aside from course work, I often settled back in my dorm room with a journal, a tablet of poetry, and a growing pile of rejection slips from the New Yorker.

In clinical work, I enjoyed deep satisfaction from helping people and analyzing medical charts. Being indoors, however, continued to bleach my mouth dry. Not only wearing shoes, but also feeling carpet under my shoes, gave me the same sensation as fingernails on a chalkboad. The classes that I did attend, I quickly attended in socks, a small revolt which other students started following. As always, it seemed, Copenhagen became a minor trend at my schools, and it was a little comical to see one of the diamond-studded young socialites on my floor walking around with a spit cup.

My white nursing shoes clocked many miles to the rhythmic clicking of my hip joint.

It restored some of my confidence to be asked on dates, by pre-law and pre-med students, and especially by officers in the maritime. Their stories of overseas adventures and deep-sea storms captured my heart. As my ten month-long clinical year came to a close, I enjoyed the memories of beaus spiriting me away in cabs for restaurants and night clubs and Broadway shows, and leaning into my eyes with marriage proposals. The flattery surprised me, but I stepped back aboard the Nanticoke with only one thought in mind: could anything really lure me from my love of the sea?

By August I had enough documented sea time to qualify for the Able Bodied seaman exam.

"Haven't you started studying yet?" Mom would step into the galley and ask.

"Golly, Mama," I'd complain from my dishes and sudsy sink. "I know boats."

"But the Coast Guard exam is not easy! Do you know the three different types of fires? What is the first thing you do to lower a lifeboat?"

"With gravity davits?"

"Yes, with gravity davits."

"Uncleat the, um, -"

"No, darling. Put in the plug. And an A.B. is licensed to command a lifeboat! Study, darling, study!"

I drew out the hand-sized Manual for Lifeboatmen, Able Seamen, and Qualified Members of the Engine Department. Jono patiently quizzed me in the evenings on the hawser table, and in a few weeks, I stepped ashore in my good shore clothes at the Norfolk grain pier.

My papers included the list of my years on our tugs as proof of sea time. Mom copied the dates longhand out of our wheel-house logs, starting from my first day on tug Babe in 1972. Dad also wrote the necessary captain's letter of endorsement.

Curious looks followed me as a woman merchant mariner in the Coast Guard building. The sun and salt had white-streaked my hair as I now stood nine inches over five feet. From the application counter, I watched the ripple of desk to desk stares and leaning heads whispering, "She's here for the A.B. exam."

*The first woman licensed tugboat operator in the
United States of America*

I was processed and given a table. My pencil lead darted cautiously at the test papers: where would you find the No.5 life-boat on a ship? No.2? What are the commands to control a boat under oars? What does the command "give way" mean? the command "toss oars"?; what types of davits are commonly found on merchant ships?; what is a tricing pendant? a frapping line?; what is the purpose of storm oil?; box the cardinal and intercardinal points of the compass; describe the Williamson Turn rescue maneuver for a man overboard; what type of extinguisher is used for an electrical fire? an oil fire?; what is the fog signal for steam vessels on the high seas?

79

Alison, the 2nd licensed Able Bodied seawoman out of Norfolk

At the miniature lifeboat section of the exam, I was observed by a starch-white cloud of Coast Guard officers with bundles of ribbons pinned to their chests. As I gave the proper orders for a lifeboat commander, I represented another moment in local maritime history. Mom was the first woman to earn her A.B.'s ticket in Norfolk, and the first woman tugboat operator in the United States; Alison was the second woman A.B. licensed in Norfolk; and now I was the third. The officers' gesture of acknowledgement was kind, and, proudly holding my laminated A.B.'s ticket, sweat pooled in my hand all the hot cab ride home.

I was briefly back in my student nursing uniform that fall.

On the first day of clinical, I looked down from a hospital obstetrics window to the East River. As I turned to follow a tug and tow, the petite woven shoulders of my uniform tightened across my hawser-hardened back. My skirt hissed softly against my stockings. Smoothing my skirt to my knees, my hand calluses snagged in the fabric.

I looked down at the East River, and sighed unhappily at the irony. I was completely accepted as a feminine woman in the merchant marine, by twice as strong and agile seamen. But back at the school dorm, more conversations awaited in an ongoing foreign language. I seemed to have a biblical lack of knowledge of make up, clothing, shampoos, dieting, soap operas, the suburbs, and weddings. Another uninterrupted summer of cooking and decking was behind me. I turned on my clicking hip, looked around the busy ward, and knew I wouldn't stay.

I worked for the rest of the semester for a marketing research firm on Lexington Avenue. In the spring, I returned to my college main campus for a variety of courses like accounting. I used my nursing education to pass the state board exam for accreditation of the LPN's license.

And my conflict between living on land or sea towered to a new height. It whipped around the direction of my destiny with it. Conversations with college career counselors seemed a little useless. Young female students could only have sea experience, they seemed to think, on weekend pleasure crafts.

I was on my own. And my destiny, I knew, as a young woman who loved the sea, was staggeringly uncharted.

Tug Nanticoke was inspected in dry dock the following summer by a perspective buyer. We looked at each other in the galley, not really seeing each other, when the buyer sat down and ate with us on the ways.

Galley mutiny - with a water pistol!

81

Mom and Dad wanted to return to the long-ignored farm and their love of standardbred horse racing. They wanted to build a state of the art horse barn. It was something they always hoped for in our impoverished years of harness racing in the 1960's.

Nanticoke on the ways

My parents, in their great friendship and love for each other, had many more adventures to undertake side by side. In five years, after success and fun in semi-retirement with the horses, they would sell the farm and live on their fifty foot sailboat in the Caribbean. Live-aboards for seventeen years, they sailed their Morgan ketch transatlantic to tour Europe.

And so my family stepped up to the dock in Seaford, from our Nanticoke's decks, for the very last time.

"Here, honey," the new captain's wife was saying to me. She was only visiting the tug, before she drove back home. "Take this."

She handed a heavy porcelain galley mug to me. With one foot on the dock, and the other on Nanticoke's rail, I reached down for the mug. I had surely filled it, and clung to it up the wheelhouse ladder, a hundred times. My eyes misted as I smiled. Lifting my foot from the rail, I joined my family on the dock.

Dad was talking to the captain, hired by the new owner, who wasn't there.

"She'll be good to you, Cap'," Dad said. He was looking up at the Nanticoke in appraisal with his hands on his hips. He was squinting, I knew, to hide his emotions. "She was damn good to us," he growled, and shook the captain's hand in final farewell.

...   .

My berth was gone!

A little more than six thousand dollars had been given to me through the 1800's Jones Act, for injured seamen. I used some of the money to buy an old vehicle and drove to the Philadelphia U.S.C.G.. I added the rate of Food Handler to my A.B.'s ticket so I could work at sea on deck or in the steward's department. And I bought a road map of the nation. In the simplicity of youthful thinking, I decided the best place to adjust to land-living would be the most wide open place.

Six months later, I was on a Houston plane bound for Philadelphia with my Texas apartment, in art deco pink, behind me. I looked down from my window on the airport tarmac. My heart was already in flight as my fingertips tapped the armrest. A ship's company had given me a position in their steward's department with hopes I'd switch to deck.

It was a wasted exercise to try to sleep in my airport motel that night. I was relieved to get started in the morning. I arrived on the Delaware River waterfront to a high tangle of towers and tanks in the pre-dawn murk. I hoisted my two duffles out of the cab. Though it was early summer, my duffles were stuffed and prepared with every type of foul weather gear. I could have weathered a voyage to the North Pole in a canoe. Gasping and turning red from the weight of my duffles, I pointed my steps toward the river.

My walk through the terminal, about an eighth of a mile, ended with ship to my left and ship to my right. I couldn't see the ends of the hull.

A tall A.B. at the top of the gangway found my name on a roster. He jerked his head for me to follow him. In a near-faint from excitement, and just about from the weight of the duffles, I stepped aboard a ship for the first time.

A vivid orange dawn painted the channel and far shore. The ship's deck hoses and shadowy wheel cranks took on the brilliant hue. The white forward house of the split-house ship stood fifty feet tall in its changing orange dress. It was buttoned with dark porthole glass, and laced in thin white catwalks. The massive bridge wings arched out silently.

The aft house, where I was being led, was a couple of stories high. A tractor trailer-sized stack stood on its top deck. I passed hundreds of feet of a single catwalk that ran down the center of the ship between the two houses. Hoses and pipes wove below it.

We descended stair after stair in the aft house until, in the familiar smell of paint and rust, the A.B. booted open a fo'c'sle door deep inside the tanker.

"All yers," he sniffed. His steps clicked away in the wide, dim hall. The hall was lined with many more doors.

I had researched my new vessel, the Delaware Sun, a six hundred and forty one foot T-5 class tanker or "baby supertanker". Her cargo capacity was two hundred and fifty thousand barrels of fuel in thirty different tanks.

The Delaware Sun carried twenty two thousand barrels of fuel oil to run two steam turbines. She was capable of thirteen thousand five hundred horsepower.

Her five blade propeller had a diameter of twenty six feet, six inches. The propeller pitch, or forward motion from one revolution of the prop, was seventeen feet.

The Nanticoke's pitch was sixty three inches.

The small fo'c'sle was familiar, however, with a bunk, sink, and locker. From the hall into my room, I dragged my duffles that were, by this time, apparently stuffed with concrete. I sat on my mattress and looked eye-level at the station bill framed at the head of my bunk. From my A.B. training, I familiarized myself with my station bill. The small paper indicated my lifeboat station and my station in a fire, with those corresponding whistle signals as well as that to abandon ship.

I opened the large porthole over the bunk. I rested my chin on the bottom rim, and stared down at the orange ripples on the

84

channel.

Soon the summer day was bright white and noisy. Officers and crew were returning from shore leave in boisterous or sullen groups.

I had found my way to the galley, located off the poop deck. In my starched white apron and long braids, I skirted behind the chief steward as crewmen roared into the mess with shore tales. Silence fell across their perspiring black and white faces to spot me by the cavernous galley sinks. I stared back in equal shock.

"A woman on the ship! There's a woman on the ship!" Voices sang and hollered aft to the poop deck and forward down the ladder wells.

"Ah, Emily?"

I looked over, a little panic-stricken, to the chief steward. He tilted his head to a large dirty pan.

"Okay, Jerry," I said courteously, though my voice slightly trembled. I sank the pan into the soapy water.

It seemed in long habit that Jerry tugged one side and then the other of his brown mustache. "After that pan, let's see you by the dishwashing machine," he said, tugging at the bushy mustache. "I'll show you how the dishwasher works."

I nodded, and scrubbed fiercely at the giant pan as I listened to the hoots and revelry of the men outside the portholes on the poop deck. The Delaware Sun was sailing in minutes! Just minutes to get my duffles - forget those duffles! - and fly back to my new Houston apartment and away from the sea forever. I'd get a cat! A dog! I'd even be a nurse!

I thought about it hard because tears were blurring my view of the sink. This was my big deep-sea adventure. Now I knew what it felt like to stand on the deck of a ship. That was enough! Now I wanted to get off! Now I -

"TOOOOOOOT!" The ship's horn boomed. I cried out, and dashed onto the poop deck.

"Haul 'er in, boys!" a barrel-chested bosun in khakis cried. "We're headin' out!"

Bare-backed crewmen heaved on a line in front of me. They

dragged it to a capstan. Swear words spat from their sweaty faces. I cowered farther and farther back into the galley doorway. The buildings and cranes on the shore were pulling away! I dabbed my apron at the tear-mixed sweat on my cheeks and peered wide-eyed at the poop deck and the half dozen, grinning sailors.

My fo'c'sle was in the far stern of the ship. It was very close to the rudder, I knew. All I could hear was the banging of the hydraulic steering gears as I perched on the edge of my bunk. My work duties were over for the day. I sat listening to the irregular thumps and jumps below the rumbling deck.

Supper had passed in sweat and noise by the dish washing machines. The many crewmen, dropping off their plates, made a range of jovial comments. I just kept working and sweating and promising myself that no one would see me cry.

Now, in the privacy of my fo'c'sle, my high chin was on my chest. I knew sailing deep-sea was a part of my destiny. I knew I had to face it as much as a bird having to fly.

Did everyone in the world, I wondered with terrible loneliness, have to reach out to their destinies with both hands? Should I have safely waited ashore for mine? Would it have found me there?

It was too late to know.

I pulled myself up to the porthole. Lights from the ship glinted off the surface of the smooth sea. I felt anxious to hear the ship's wake whispering so many stories below. Passed my knitted eyebrows, the infinity of night had fallen across the Atlantic, and had taken my little porthole, and the massive ship, along with it.

···   ···   ···   ···   ···

Jerry assigned me to the mess hall for petty officers the next day. Petty officers were not officers but of a higher rate than ordinaries, A.B.'s and engine room wipers. The bosun, pumpmen, quartermaster, and electricians would eat in my assigned station.

In a short voyage, we rounded the coast and made port in New Jersey. My confidence took a small leap. Apparently, the Delaware Sun made port often.

I had taken notice of my surroundings in detail by New Jersey. The table cloths in the unlicensed mess were tattered. No pretty pictures hung on the bulkheads. There was no sign of warmth within the utilitarian, gray-painted walls.

"Comin' ashore, Emily?" the rotund cook was asking me in the mess hall. Willy had been very kind. He gestured to some other steward department members. "Come ashore with us."

"All right, Willy," I answered, pleased to be included. "I'll meet you at the gangway." I hurried below to my fo'c'sle for some money and my penknife.

The ship's most popular tavern was a few streets up from the pier and revelry was in full swing. The crew was polite to me, and very respectful. I was surprised and pleased that they didn't infringe on me in any way.

I might have infringed on the crew when I returned to the ship. My arms were filled with blue and yellow flowered weeds. I had cut them from the riverbank with my penknife. Growing up with red gingham curtains on the portholes, I never knew that merchant vessels had to be cold. But a young third mate took quick umbrage.

"What is this?!" square, muscular Brett snarled. He stood in the mess hall with one arm extended back and the other lurched forward in a jab, like he was in a fencing match. He pointed an accusing finger at some flowers. They were next to my collection of jars on the tables, for vases, from the galley.

I was adding the last touches to an arrangement but suddenly looked up. "I-I.. you don't like the flowers, third?" I lowered my jar to a table.

"Not on my goddamn ship!"

I gasped. I looked down. "Well, I.." After a moment, I picked up a jar and walked to the doorway of the poop deck. "I guess I'll throw them over."

The half dozen crewmen in the mess looked from Brett to

me, and then stared back at him for his response. "Hey!" he was protesting. "Now wait a minute."

I wasn't sure what to say to the officer. "I mean, but- that's what you want."

"Oh, all right, all right," Brett suddenly muttered. He strutted up to a bouquet and said, "You can keep the damn - you can keep the flowers." Then he put his hands on his hips and jutted out his chin. "But this is still a goddamn ship!"

Somehow that did it for me, looking at the muscular officer by the jar of droopy weeds. I started chuckling and brought my fingertips to hide my smile. Of all the years I had sailed, to end here now, on a dangerous vessel of fuel tanks bound for sea with an officer enraged over flowers? It was the kind of laughter, in that kind of moment, where no one could really resist the release of tension. Soon the whole mess hall was ringing with the contagious laughter, with even some hearty guffawing, including, and most of all, from Brett himself.

Seeing the flowers for the first time, not all the crew was chuckling at breakfast.

As we were making Verrazano Narrows Bridge, the comments snapped out from the crowded tables. "Ain't no goddamn tea party.." "Shouldn't be no women on a ship in the first place.."

Some of the seamen, however, swigged their coffee with the softest looks of contentment on their grizzled faces. Tatooed and grease-smeared, they nodded their heads at the little weeds with approval.

The Statue of Liberty hung off our ship for a day and a night. New York City looking in my porthole was a familiar face to see. Although my insomnia was continuing, my nervousness to be on the ship was easing. Then, of course, we sailed for the Bermuda Triangle.

...   .

Captain Taylor was ten feet tall. Maybe he was closer to six foot two, but he seemed a lot taller when he did room checks off

88

the coast.

I was struggling to escape my insomnia and fall asleep with a book. Scattered throughout my small fo'c'sle were the results of my duffles, the contents of which could have supplied an outdoors shop. The fan in my room was broken, and I looked up through my sweat at the sudden invasion at the doorway, at the towering captain and his entourage. I didn't have any hidden illegal cargo, like drugs or alcohol, but I was awfully embarrassed by the messy state of my fo'c'sle.

Captain Taylor somberly glanced over the heaps of clothing and left. Jerry lingered in the doorway. He looked concerned.

"Oh, Jerry!" I gasped. His sympathetic look collapsed the dam to my tears, and they welled up quickly in my eyes. "My room! The captain! I-I.."

"It's okay, Emily," Jerry said. He lowered his clipboard and waved a hand through the air. "Don't worry about the captain." He turned to go, and then leaned back into the doorway. "And, how about you try and get some sleep?"

"Don't sweat it, Em," John advised. The lanky blonde A.B. and Viet Nam vet rubbed his freshly shaven face on the capstan seat. "I don't sleep until the third day out or so."

"Is that right?" I replied. I rubbed my eyes in the morning sun. Sighing, I switched my mop handle to my other arm on the poop deck.

"You'll get your sleep. You have to get used to the feel of the ship first, that's all."

I followed John's eyes to the west, away from the slanting sun, where the eastern seaboard should have been. There was nothing on the flat horizon. I looked up at him with my puffy eyes. "You know, John, it's so strange out here. There's something missing." I looked at the endless blue ocean. I had never seen anything so big in my life. "What's missing.." I thought aloud. I rubbed my eyes again. The size of the ocean was dizzying, and my exhaustion was making it all the more strange.

John chuckled. "Not a newstand in sight, is that it?"

Willy stepped out of the galley with a bucket. The giant cook nodded at us. He waddled to the end of the poop deck, thirty feet above the prop wash. Willy emptied his bucket, nodded again, and returned to the galley. I grinned at John and pointed down to the powerful wake. "That's it!" I snapped my fingers. "No sea gulls!"

"That's right. Gulls stick to the coast." John stretched and hopped down to the deck. "I'll catch you later. Time for watch."

I reached down for my bucket. No sea gulls!

No sea gulls and no coast.

No coast, and no Chesapeake Bay, and no Miss Debbie! In all of my excitement and daring to go on a ship, the reality of the adventure finally, simply struck. My breathing went shallow. How did I manage to put myself on this iron continent with thirty five men?

Alone on the poop deck, I cursed my curiosity with a hand to my forehead. What in the world had I done? Who were these strangers holding this ship, and my life, in their hands?

I turned back to the empty horizon, now with a board-straight spine.

...   .

We did not collide, run aground, capsize, break up, or otherwise slobber below the cold surface of the ocean by Port Everglades. Five days had passed. We paralleled Florida's pencil-line of white beaches and the baby blue shoals to our next port. Clear waters hugged our ship. Palm trees dotted the terminal. I bought a book ashore, pleased to size up my new adventure from the ground for an hour.

The Delaware Sun steamed deeper and deeper into a rich, southward longitude to the Virgin Pass. The penetrating heat seemed to blend the days together in a bright, walking dream. Seas shimmered around us in moving blues and greens I had never before seen.

"What's the name of it?" I hushed to Limey on the poop deck.

The plump English ordinary leaned back leisurely on his bench seat. "She's cawl't Sail Rock, she is." Limey scratched his curly gray hair and raised his chin in appraisal. "Pretty enou' sight!"

"Yea!" I said, and smiled at the white triangle jutting up on the horizon. At first it was a schooner, angling through the seas. It grew larger off our starboard deck as we passed, and showed wrinkles and crevaces across its jagged shape.

The island of St. Thomas wavered in deep green on our port. The sky was clear except for a mustache of white clouds over the island. We would reach landfall that night, scuttlebutt said.

And we did. Necklesses of tiny lights draped high and low over the close horizon. The night was moonless. We powered back and forth slowly waiting for our berth to open.

I decided to join a handful of crew on the bow during our wait. Before I started the long walk forward, a seaman warned me to be careful on the bow. I told him thanks, but wondered if he really thought I could manage to fall overboard. That was one thing I knew how *not* to do.

I thought I did.

A fifteen knot wind coursed powerfully over the bow deck like a pushing river. I wanted to lean against the chest-high rail like the other crew there, but felt my legs being dragged toward an open, barrel-sized line chock. I understood the seaman's warning. The chock on the high deck created a funnel of wind I had never experienced on a deck. The force of the suction, from the deck to the chock and out to the night sea, alarmed me. I didn't know if the force could suddenly increase, or, despite my well-toned body, if I could resist it. Surprised to encounter such a basic limit to my strength on the ship, and especially on such a peaceful night, I returned aft.

The low lights of a laden tanker finally slid out from the shore. It passed us into the obscurity of the night. We powered at a crawl to our open berth, and at dawn, I stretched up to my port-hole from my sheets in one movement. A white sun was rising. It burned at a mist beside the ship. The mist spread like a slow-swirling dancer's skirt, and lapped into the lush green mountains of Puerto Rico.

I took a terminal van to explore the port of Yabucoa. It was snuggled into the slope of a mountain side. The village had narrow, uneven sidewalks that tapered into heaps of pebbles on the narrow streets. A cloud of children followed my exploration of the village. I stopped and called Mom and Dad at the farm. The children cavorted around the phone booth. Little girls touched their thick dark hair and pointed to my blonde braids. I pointed to their hair, and comically looking up at the sky, I sighed as if their hair was too pretty for words. We laughed at the exchange of our skits and off they ran to play. I stepped along to the village square, with an old man as a constant feature trailing five feet behind me.

The first display at an open market was a heap of thong sandals. They spilled against an oleaginous pile of pig snouts, next to long cabbages and freckled carrots and a jumble of New York Yankee baseball caps. Buildings squeezed together and lined the streets at the square, warmed with a crumbling statue at its center. Brightly dressed tenants leaned and watched from warped balconies, and it was relaxing for me to rest under a palm tree in the square.

The Green Tree was a shack. It had a dozen folding tables, folding chairs, two dangling light bulbs, and a floor fan. The crew headed to the Green Tree at night for warm rum or warm beer or to just get off the ship. I joined the migration with Willy and the steward department gang, with our card deck.

"Come on and deal, Emily!" Georgie demanded. He leaned forward in his chair and spied the table top impatiently. "It's your deal!"

"Roger, roger!" I laughed. The legs of my folding chair scraped over the wooden floor as I repositioned myself to the wobbly table. Willy returned with a handful of plastic cups as we glistened with sweat over the landing moist cards.

"Hey, Stew!" Willy called out to one of the cadets. "How about another song? Any country music?"

"Oh, wow! No way!" Stewart laughed over the milling crowd, and soon the voice of Diana Ross was crying around us into the tropic heat. A crowd of islanders entered the front door, which courageously hung by one hinge. Before long, reggae music peppered its rhythm from the juke box into the hot, smokey tavern.

"Hey, Stew!" Georgie cried suddenly, and leaned across the table with a grin. He slapped his cards to the table. Stewart, a usually quiet and bespectacled cadet, had taken up the center of the floor. Across from him, a shiny dark lady pulsated in her bright dress as they danced, shoulders back, hips jarring to the beat.

The night thundered in the old shack, which luckily, if not strategically, leaned into a mountain and not away from it.

Our hull sank under the harsh Puerto Rican sun until we were laden with cargo and pressing northward, forty feet deep through the ocean's powerful currents. Off-watch crew would occasionally gather on the stack deck where we leaned against the rails and talked, and looked out at the sparkling ocean. We were alone for six days. The sole sign of life was plant life streaking the ocean's surface. The crew called the long strings of brown plants sargasso weeds. I didn't see any whales, dolphins, or turtles, but a lot of the sargasso weeds and my mop.

A heavy fog welcomed us on the Delaware Bay. Our deep and trembling fog horn sounded hour after hour as we edged slow ahead. The measured horn taunted growing onboard anticipation to make home port. When a sea gull dashed out of the mist passed the poop deck, my heart started. Landfall!

I paced with my shipmates. Channel fever! Assignment changes and shore leaves were brought down by messenger from the captain's quarters. They were yelled out from the mess bulletin board. I hurried in the excitement to my fo'c'sle to pack for a visit to Alison.

Sharing a house with several other students, Alison stopped and stared when she opened her door, at the darkness of my skin and the vanilla streaks of my sun-washed hair. Our conversations were filled with memories, laughter, and excitement of the present, as I told her of my first voyage across the ocean and the faraway village I explored across it.

The forty eight hour pass ended quickly. Alison and I walked and talked and soon hugged goodbye. Back on the ship, I tossed my duffle onto my bunk thoughtfully. My shore visit had reminded me of the purpose of my sea adventure. I needed to choose my destiny once and for all between the sea and shore.

Alison, owing it mostly to her seasickness, had made the transition to land easily. When would I? I wondered, too, how much would I miss by coming ashore, like the discovery of something so new and so beautiful as the gentle, faraway village of Yabucoa, sleeping beside its crystal waves?

...   .

"Good job, Tom!"

The six foot quartermaster, built like a boxer, slapped the rail and said, "Emily! All right! I steered this old ship right to the dock!"

"You got it, Tom!"

By my second voyage, shipboad routine was easing my singularity among the men. We knew each other's responsibilities, and would compliment each other, or console each other over a work skirmish. With this self-consciousness reduced, I gave more attention to my surroundings on our return to Yabucoa.

Flamboyan tree blossoms were scattered in orange-red flames beside our ship in the terminal. I stepped down the gangway to explore them with my long apron flipping beneath my galley knife.

Beyond the scrawny cattle in an unfenced field by the terminal, towering ceiba trees stood in a line in the distance. The ceiba trees, which some of the crew called God trees, looked like giant conferring elephants. I skipped with excitement across the parched grasses. From my maritime upbringing with my parents, the water was meant for singing as much as for commerce. I dipped my apron by the bright Caribbean sea and chirped all the high notes I could reach. My symphony with nature tumbled happily up to the bright flamboyan blossoms. I curtsied in silly formalness to a tree, scooted under its shade, and screamed!

Snakes! Everywhere! Hanging from the branches! I leapt back

94

with my knife in front of my face.

The snakes didn't move. They weren't snakes at all. They were pods, thick and dark, dangling from the branches and laying on the ground. I gave a nervous laugh but stayed where I was. I reached out and tapped a pod with my knife. Shiny seeds scattered to the dirt at my feet. I picked them up and rolled the dirt off in my palm. The seeds were oblong and black, and they tapped together like smooth beads. They were beautiful, and I cut a pod from a branch to keep before I reached to the bursts of orange-red blossoms. I filled my apron to overflowing and returned to the ship.

Leaning against the ship's rail, a seaman on watch rolled his eyes and groaned, "Not again!" But the other crew on deck just chuckled at my slow, fluffy-orange ascent up the gangway.

Now I had enough flowers, real flowers, too, for the officers' saloon.

Round tables were bolted to the deck of the officers' saloon and surrounded by leather chairs. The saloon's regular messman, Peaches, wore a stiff, white uniform when he served meals to the officers there.

Soon the officers' saloon, the petty officers' mess, and the crew's mess all had bright orange flamboyan arrangements on their tables. The petals were vivid in the sunlight from the portholes. Through the open doors, the sea streaked in light and dark blues aft our berth, and provided a stunning background to the orange-red illuminations of the table bouquets.

There might have been less conflict about new table bouquets, but there was a brand new storm brewing on the ship. It was in the steward's department. It came in the form of Peaches' replacement during his time off. Rona had boarded when we left Marcus Hook. She was a middle aged woman who didn't befriend anyone and seemed to want to throttle people who were polite to her.

If that was enough tension generally, Rona also tried to get others to do her work. Confrontations with her steadily increased, and I altogether enjoyed avoiding Rona. Her presence, however, could have been an omen of bad things to come. I didn't think so at the time. I didn't think my deep-sea adventure would soon end.

The next day in Yabucoa, on a Friday the thirteenth, a wiper fell in the engine room and broke his arm in two places. Willy's assistant cook suddenly teared and lisped with a bad toothache. And, I was next.

I was in the terminal van filled with crew returning from the village. The young cadet Jacob sat across the aisle in the van. He was holding a soggy paper bag in his lap and looked nervous.

I pointed to his six pack of ten ounce beer. "That bag's breaking, Jacob," I said with practicality. "I'll take it aboard for you, in my bandanna." And I did, up the gangway and under the empty bridge wings.

The bridge wings were not empty. I handed the beer to Jacob in the crew hallway as one of the thirds stepped reluctantly toward us. "Ah, the captain saw you, Emily, from up above. I've got to take the beer."

"It's mine, Brett, I swear," the cadet asserted. "Emily didn't know anything about it. She just brought it aboard for me, from the van."

"I'm sorry," Brett said. "I really am." He turned up the hallway with the soggy bag. I shook out my bandanna behind him, and shook my shoulders.

Less than twenty four hours out of port, Rona declared she had a heart attack. I assisted the chief officer with my nursing training in Rona's fo'c'sle.

Rona had a regular heartbeat. She was alert and talkative. Her pupils weren't dilated. Her fingernails returned good color. She was in great shape. She insisted on leaving the tanker, however. Captain Taylor, despite appearing as skeptical as his chief officer of the heart attack claim, left Rona's room to change course.

San Juan's lights filled the horizon in the following hours. Brightly lit passenger ships glided by us. They shimmered and reflected on the night waters. Their hulls turned and winked with the lights of hundreds of portholes. Unlike our wall-like hull, containing different grades of fuel, the passenger vessels had cargoes of life, dancing, laughing, and dining over the ocean swells. I joined several crew standing quietly on deck. We rested our forearms on the rails and watched the passing vessels of more luxurious worlds.

Rona emerged on deck with her suitcases. From her frightened appearance, it seemed she might have a real heart attack.

The gangway wasn't there at all. A flat, rope Jacob's ladder dropped from the deck to the sea. Bounding up to our side was a tugboat showing one light on its wheelhouse mast.

I turned on the deck, and watched Rona clutch the back of the chief officer's khaki shirt. The chief officer wasn't acting terribly sympathetic. If Rona had insisted on leaving the ship in Yabucoa, she'd have been responsible for her fare home. Instead she stopped a six hundred foot tanker under the guise of a medical emergency.

I stepped down the deck and talked to an off-watch member of the engine gang. He told me that a ship can't just stop, but that several engine room personnel must be stationed to open and close the valves that run and reduce the steam engine's power. After slowing down from sea speed, a ship needed the minimum maneuverable speed of three knots.

At this speed, then, through the sleepy Caribbean swells, we ran with the tug and gave up our feisty saloon steward. I didn't know I would be taking her place.

···   ···   ···   ···   ···

"We're gonna miss you, Emily!" Tom bawled in the crew's mess.

"Why?" I asked. "Because I'll be serving the officers?"

"Naw!" B.J. spat. The ordinary looked up from a poker game at a nearby table. "'Cause you're gettin' fired!"

"Fired? What on earth for?"

"For that beer thing, that's what for!"

Tom said, "Don't listen to him, Em. Salt water's on his brain."

"Well," contributed Limey, "'e might be right."

"Not you, too, Limey!" I cried. "Fire me? Over that? It wasn't even my beer."

"It's a company ship, not union like the war. An' that's the truth, it is."

Scuttlebutt grew to hound me. Tables held court in weighing my fate, and silenced self-consciously when I approached. The messman who cleaned the captain's quarters, "official memo reader", apologized for finding no inside scoop.

Captain Taylor was maintaining a mysterious silence of my fate. My imagination grew to include a keel-hauling sentence at dawn. It was all the more awkward, then, when I stepped into the saloon the following evening and served the ship's officers for the first time.

...   .

Unlike the crew and petty officers' mess, there were no cheerful conversations in the saloon. The comfortable talks I had had with the chief officer or the third engineer on the poop deck had no registry in the saloon. Dinners were ordered from a typed menu at each table in monotone voices.

Then the captain arrived. The hushed mood became funereal. Junior officers dedicated themselves quietly to their plates with lowered heads. The captain passed the junior officers without looking at them and lumbered across the saloon to the largest table. He joined the chief mate, as well as Harry, the chief engineer, and the spark.

An occasional howl curled through the saloon and told of building weather. The water I had poured into their glasses slopped from side to side. The officers indifferently, and silently, ate.

Turning various shades of red, I crossed the rocking deck and approached Captain Taylor's table.

"I'll have," the captain's deep voice was suddenly rumbling, "the steak." He gave a slight grin to Harry and looked up at me. "Medium rare. The brocolli. Rice." He flipped down his menu next to the flamboyan blossoms and crossed his hands.

"Medium," the old engineer was saying. "A salad."

"Same as Harry's," said the spark.

98

I unglued my eyes from the captain and left.

Jerry was clutching a sink for balance with one hand and furiously tugging at his mustache with the other. "What did he order, Emily? Think!" the chief steward cried, swaying out from the sink with the seas.

"Jerry! Jerry! Jerry!" I screeched in the crashing, steamy galley. "Was it rare? Was it well-done? Was that Harry's order?

Jerry grabbed his head in disbelief and walked in several tight circles. He smacked his hands to his sides. "You're- you're-" he blustered, "going to have to go back in!"

"No, Jerry!"

"Ask again, Emily! And for crying out loud," he said, pressing his fingertips to his temples, "remember the captain's order!"

"Willy!" I cried at the cook. Willy just shook his sweaty head, the poop deck rising above the horizon behind him.

"Captain Taylor?"

The low conversation stopped. The officers looked up from their empty table. The junior officers leaned back in their chairs and looked over.

"Could you repeat your order, Captain Taylor?" I asked. My eyes slightly, painfully rolled. My long apron was swaying with the seas, and I held the table edge by my fingertips for balance. He rubbed his nose, very slowly, and repeated his order. I silently mouthed his words again and again as I weaved from handhold to handhold back to the galley.

The seas banked up heavier swells into the night. I was taking comfort in the privacy of my fo'c'sle from the embarrassing events of dinner, which now no longer mattered because I decided the ship was sinking.

The pen rolled off the journal in my lap. At my back, the bulkhead ruggedly registered the ship's bow jerking in one direction, and then another, before sending the stress back along its ribs. The great tanker seemed to be managing the seas in sections. How I could feel it, that distant jarring, followed by another, closer, and another, until the welded beams battled the stress to the stern. Again and again the big ship seemed to spiral through the seas.

This was new to me. Tugs hit waves in one fist, not an elongation of steel parts promising to stay together. I crawled on hands and knees down my bunk to the porthole. I wrapped my fingers onto the bottom rim.

The ocean bellied up hissing and whispering three yards below my porthole on the laden ship. Salt air whipped at my nose. I peered over my fingers at the black seas. A loose collection of blonde grass twisted by and vanished in the skimming circle of my porthole light.

Giving up my self-imposed exile, I teetered through the hallway with a desire to be up above. I found company on the deck of the aft house. Locking our arms on the rail, cadet Jacob and I looked forward at the wash pouring over our midships, over the valves and hoses and across the deck in ghostly, twirling white. Jacob and I shouted over the strong, warm wind as we pointed at the decks of the rocking ship.

A figure appeared. The man was walking forward and stopping for balance on the long center catwalk. His shoulders and gait could have belonged to one of the third mates.

"But look, Jacob!" I yelled into his ear. "He's smoking a cigarette! He has a lit cigarette!"

"Holy crap!" Jacob shouted, and like me, leaned his head back instinctively in anticipation of a blast. Sparks from the man's cigarette leapt and scattered in red specks across the loaded tanks.

The ship slowed and its horns blasted for a fire drill the next day. As a member of the apparently expendable steward's department, my station was dead-center of our laden tanks.

I manned a heavy black hose mid-point of the long, center catwalk. I stood at attention with the hose, and squinted against the sunshine and the becalmed, glimmering ocean. The deck crew gathered below me at the lifeboats. I could see them testing the frapping lines and davit gears. I wished I was working with them, and felt a pang of regret to avoid deck action because of the winch wheel. Instead I was in the steward's department, and stationed with irrelevance at the bull's eye of the laden tanks.

Jacob trotted across the deck. "It was Mark, the cadet!" he called up in a loud whisper. "But I already talked to the third about it. Brett's not going to tell the captain, 'cause Mark would be in really hot water for that cigarette!"

I nodded, but smiled a little weakly with memories of how scary the cigarette was to see.

"It's okay!" Jacob continued, reading my face. "Brett's had a smart talk with him!" And I nodded again with more reassurance.

We continued at emergency stations. Captain Taylor's form floated from bridge wing to bridge wing in frowning observation. Our orange life jackets were bulky and heavy, and everyone was shiny with perspiration in the sun. Eventually Captain Taylor disappeared to the bridge. Three short horn blasts charged across the empty ocean, dismissing us.

We powered on for five days.

Scuttlebutt had so tantalized the anticipation of my fate that my knees actually, slightly dipped, from weakness, when the messenger finally came to the galley on the last day of the voyage. I prayed no one had noticed.

"Emily," the messenger said hesitantly. Faces looked up in the crew's mess. "The captain.." he said. He had no need to finish his sentence. Activity at the mess tables stopped. I put down a salt box I was holding. I put down the shaker I was filling. Wiping the salt from my hands, I returned the stares with a lift of my eyebrows and a brave smile to my mates.

I walked forward on the long catwalk. This was it.

Each seaman received a paycheck and discharge paper at the end of the voyage. The discharges, light green and a little larger than personal bank checks, were proof of seatime for license upgrading with the Coast Guard. I was to receive my paycheck and voyage discharge in a private audience to accommodate my long awaited reprimand.

A shiver ran through my shoulders at the end of the catwalk. Would I be reprimanded in front of a group of officers? How offended was the captain, by this broken rule of his ship? I tried to take a deep breath but only gasped a couple of times at the bottom of an inner ladder well.

I ran out of ladder well at a wide passageway. It led to a linoleum deck, glittering with polish. A brass shrubbery of instruments and control panels filled the wide bridge. I was at the door of the bridge! "Hey, Sammy!" I called to the second. "Hey, Brett! This is a wonderful bridge! Wow! It's really big! It's really-"

"Hey, Cinderella," the spark growled behind me. He jerked a thumb at a nearby door with a brass plate. It read CAPTAIN. I stared at the door knob.

My nose hit the powerful air-conditioning first. My fingers fell to the apron knot behind my back, and slipping down the crisp apron, I felt naked in my sweat-stained work clothes. I had entered a sleep chamber seven-times larger than my fo'c'sle. Tucking in my chin, I slightly leaned my head away from the vast, paper-covered desk in the center of the room and the captain's foreboding scowl behind it.

Captain Taylor was studying a paper. I slid breathlessly into the leather armchair across from his desk. After a full minute, he finally looked up.

I tried to look back but my sweaty arms and legs had slid straight down in the leather and I was sinking. The armchair was swallowing me. I hadn't sat in a backed chair for more than a month, just benches, and my braids were pushing into my sunburnt shoulders. My legs were itching from the cold air-conditioning, and I was twisting to scratch my back and-

"I know everything that goes on on my ship."

I froze, in the shape of a pretzel.

"This is your pay. This is your verification of seatime."

The captain extended the papers across the desk. I took them with my fingertips, and the captain was suddenly filling the ceiling. He took titan steps to the door. Like the hurried, quivering smoke from a ship's stack, I followed.

The passageway dimmed when he filled the doorway to an upper catwalk. I stepped behind him onto the catwalk, and breaking my gaze from his shoulder, I was looking at a beautiful ship.

My breathing stopped. I had never seen the Delaware Sun from the forward house. The tanker filled out my sight. She looked powerful and victorious against the endless horizon.

The captain wasn't going anywhere as he held the rail before him and looked out from his great height. I was glad he was staying. Motionless beside him, with my tangled braids and skinny, sunburnt legs, I was suspended in awe.

I never dreamed I could feel again the personal strength I had felt on the decks of tug Babe and tug Nanticoke. With no warning at all, my years as a seawoman pulled together into one sense of accomplishment. This is what I had sailed to find. I needed to feel this from the sea once more, if for the last time, in my young life. Standing next to the captain above the ocean, a great burden lifted from me.

Captain Taylor, wordless beside me, was the best career councelor I'd ever had. Command of this ship was his life's achievement, and land or sea, our accomplishments defined us. That catwalk on the Delaware Sun held me up to see mine.

I looked from Captain Taylor's square chin to his ship, and out to the clean, empty Atlantic. Zeke suddenly lifted his beard and laughed in my thoughts. And there was Mom and Dad, and Alison and our spit contests; spinning propeller shafts and spinning winch wheels; carpeted dorm rooms and the gazing eyes of beaus. And here I was, driven deep-sea to understand my unique strengths as a seawoman.

Where would that strength take me next?

Captain Taylor hooked his thumbs in his belt. His chest puffed with confidence and authority as his eyes ran over his ship in the raw sea air. But when our eyes met, he gave me a fatherly smile. He turned and filled the doorway, and vanished from the brightness where I stood.

"Aw, golly, Em!" the big quartermaster bawled. Tom shook my shoulders with his shovel hands. "You get off, I get off! I'll stand up for you!"

"Oh, Tom!" I laughed affectionately. "I can handle it. Please don't do anything like that." I poked his arm with a gentle fist, and smiled an unspoken thanks.

He smacked the bulletin board, lightly for him, which still caused it to tremble on its bulkhead hook. "But transferred! Over some stupid cadet's beer!"

Shaking our heads, Tom and I stepped out to the poop deck. I didn't tell him I was signing off the company roster. I had declined the company's offer, to sign on a sister ship on the Gulf run.

I didn't know how to tell my protective shipmate I was excited to be going ashore. In the final moments of my last maritime frontier, I didn't want to talk about leaving the sea, or the tough, trained seamen, like my family, who faced her. I just want to be a part of it all one more hour.

Tom and I thoughtfully leaned our elbows on the rail. The Delaware River terminal spread out below us.

At a corner of its tall, tarry jungle, a tugboat jarred against a dock with a passing wake. It was the prim Caroline S., of the Chesapeake Bay!

I slapped the rail!

"Tom!" I laughed. "I know that pretty tug!" I hurried through the galley. "I know that tug, Willy!"

I had seen her a hundred times in ports and rivers on the Chesapeake. How many times had I exchanged waves with her crew, and tied for supplies at the same wharf? Her red house was a happy, familiar sight.

My steps echoed through the corridors of the ship. I dashed forward, and bundled my apron at my stomach. I dodged through flying chipping hammers and the bustling deck activity, and hurried to the gangway.

My braids flipped at my shoulders. They jumped at my sun-burnt cheeks. I skipped down the gangway to the dock.

The cook on the Caroline S. was stepping on deck. He hiked over the galley coaming. He was looking up, with a broad smile, and waving his dish towel back and forth over his head.

"Hey, there!" he was shouting to me. "Where have you been?!"